A Guide to Fishing Boats and Their Gear

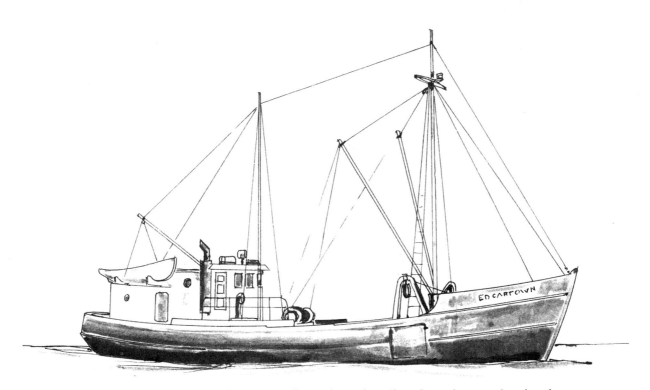

New England Dragger. Rigged as a scalloper, she carries gallows forward, port and starboard. A dredge (fig. 17) is towed from each gallows block. The otter trawler has two gallows on a side.

(On the Title Page)

Sailing out of Fleetwood, *Winmarleigh* typifies the modern British side trawler. Boat crane, radar, diesel propulsion, and kingposts distinguish her from the pre-World War II steam trawler (fig. 30).

A GUIDE TO
FISHING BOATS
AND THEIR GEAR

By Carvel Hall Blair and Willits Dyer Ansel

Cornell Maritime Press, Inc. • Cambridge, Maryland
1968

Library of Congress Catalog Card Number: 68-19048
Manufactured in the United States of America

Mon Dieu, votre mer est si grand et mon bateau est si petit.

Breton prayer

This book is dedicated to those who go to sea in small ships.

Contents

Introduction

When a man of war steams over the horizon or moors at the next pier, the mariner can always "look her up in Jane's." The classic *Fighting Ships* will tell him the displacement, armament, and machinery of every warship afloat. When he sights a fishing fleet, on the other hand, his chart table holds no such information. On a very modest basis this volume attempts to do for the world's fishing boats what Mr. Jane and his successors have done for naval vessels.

Fig. 2. Italian Inshore Stern Trawler. This type of stern trawler operates in the Tyrrhenian Sea. It tows a single trawl, leading the warps over the stern by blocks mounted on davits.

Superficially similar, fishing craft are actually as different from one another as battleships from destroyers. The doryman, when called a trawler, must feel the same annoyance as the captain who hears his cruiser called a boat. But there are more compelling reasons for correct nomenclature. Centuries of experience have taught that there must be no *things* at sea. Every ship that floats and every piece of her gear has a name. Ambiguity can cause embarrassment or even disaster. The navigator who takes *feet* for *fathoms;* the bos'n who *slacks* a mooring line when told to *check* it; the helmsman who puts his tiller to *weather* on the order *hard alee*—all

Fig. 1. British M.F.V. The Motor Fishing Vessel is a small inshore craft adapted for seines, drift nets, or other rigs that do not require high-power engines. The small deckhouse set well aft is typical of British boats.

place their craft in jeopardy. Nautical terminology is sometimes coarse . . . jackass, buttock lines, hermaphrodite, and often colorful . . . samson post, spindrift, wing and wing—but always precise. It behooves the professional seaman to learn the names of the fishing boats with which he shares the seas.

Fig. 3. South African Stern Trawler. Small trawlers like this 65-footer fish for hake and whitefish off the west coast from Capetown to Walvis Bay. The trawl is hauled on board up an inclined stern slipway.

The International Rules of the Road, moreover, require that "All vessels not engaged in fishing . . . shall, when under way, keep out of the way of vessels engaged in fishing." To keep out of the way of a fishing craft one must know what type of equipment he is using. A trawler's gear, for example, is astern; a drifter's is ahead of him. Hence one should pass ahead of a trawler, astern of a drifter. Since trawl and nets are invisible from an approaching ship, one must determine from the looks of a fisherman what he is, what he is doing, and what he is likely to do next.

A final raison d'etre for a book about fishing boats is their appeal. Landsman and seaman, professional and amateur, all enjoy the color of a fishing harbor, appreciate the workmanlike design of the boats, and admire the hardihood of their crews. Ships and boats are fun to look at, either in the water or in the pages of a book. If this guide provides an afternoon's enjoyment in an armchair or makes a bridge watch pass more quickly, it will have attained its chief objective.

Fig. 4. Doryman. Portuguese four-masters fish the Grand Banks by dory-tended longlines. European dories are one-man boats; New Englanders used two-man dories.

Chapter I describes the basic methods of the commercial fisherman and explains the equipment he uses. Understanding the gear is prerequisite to understanding the boats, for the gear strongly affects their design and operation. Each succeeding chapter discusses and illustrates one of the important types of fishermen: trawlers, hook and liners, gill netters, seiners, harpooners, support ships, research vessels, and small craft. A glossary explains terms not covered elsewhere, and a bibliography refers to books, reports, and periodicals containing further information. Finally an index lists all craft and equipment described in the text.

The research for this guide took place in the library, at sea, and on the wharves and quays of a dozen waterfronts. Some of the information came from written matter and photographs, some from observation, and some from memory. If they have made any errors, the authors would like to hear of them.

C.H.B.
W.D.A.

Fig. 5. British Freezer Stern Trawler. The "H" preceding her bow number shows that *Cape Kennedy* sails out of Hull. Her cruises last as long as six weeks and take her westward to Greenland and the Newfoundland Banks or eastward to the White Sea.

I. Methods of Fishing and Types of Gear

Fishing boats are functional: their design and construction are functions of their intended use. The primary design determinants are fishing grounds and length of cruise. Thus a French longliner working the Grand Banks is a large rugged craft with long endurance and capable of crossing the rough North Atlantic. A Chesapeake Bay crab trapper, on the other hand, is a small boat for one-day trips in land-locked waters. Within the broad limits set by these two parameters, it is the type of fishing gear that dictates the design. To understand fishing boats, then, one must first understand fishing methods and equipment.

There are many ways to catch fish, for there are dozens of species and they are taken by fishermen of at least a hundred nations. Methods can be grouped into categories according to the type of equipment and the kind of fishery.

The commercial fisherman divides his fish, from an environmental point of view, into demersal and pelagic fisheries. Demersal species or ground fish are those which live chiefly on or near the bottom of the sea (fig. 8). Pelagic species are those taken in the upper layers or at the surface (fig. 24). Fish of both types may also spend part of their lives in the middle strata of the sea, but they are hard to catch there. The midwaters lack an upper boundary like the surface or a lower boundary like the sea bottom—interfaces which the fisherman utilizes to set his gear in the respective habitats of pelagic and demersal fish. To take midwater fish, the fisherman must know the depth of the school of fish and then must be able to place his nets at the same depth. Only

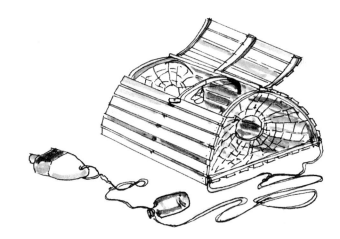

Fig. 6. Lobster Pot. Pots take a variety of shapes—hemispheres, half cylinders, oblongs. Long-lasting plastic is replacing wood in some fisheries. Each owner has a distinctive pattern for his buoys.

1

recently, with the development of fish-finder sonar and controlled depth nets, has he had this ability.

Types of fishing equipment fall into four categories: (a) nets, (b) hook and line, (c) impaling instruments, and (d) traps or pots. Table I lists the most common methods, and Chapter I describes each method with its characteristic gear.

Nets take a variety of forms. The important features of a net are the size and type of its mesh, its shape, its dimen-

Table I

	Pelagic Fisheries	Demersal Fisheries
Entangling nets	Drift nets	Bottom set nets
Surrounding nets	Seines	Bottom trawls
	Midwater trawls	Dredges
		Danish seine nets
Hook and lines	Long lines	Long lines
	Trollers	Bottom fishing
	Tuna jigs	
Impaling gear	Harpoons	
Pots, traps, etc.	Pound nets	Crab traps
		Lobster pots
		Oyster tongs
Species	Mackerel	Cod
	Herring	Halibut
	Tuna	Flounder
	Menhaden	Haddock
	Albacore	Hake
	Salmon	Ocean perch
	Sardine	Pollock
	(fig. 24)	Whitefish
		Shellfish
		(fig. 8)

sions, and its mode of employment. Table I divides nets into those which entangle the catch and those which enclose it. The first group includes gill nets and trammel nets. Rectangular in shape, these nets are designed to entangle fish that attempt to swim through the mesh. There they remain until the fisherman hauls his net and removes each fish by hand or by a power operated net shaker. The gill net is a single wall of webbing whose mesh is sized to take a particular size fish. The mesh is big enough to pass the fish's

Fig. 7. Lock-knot Sheet Bend. A knot used in making nets. Synthetic fibers are often used for greater strength and lighter weight.

head and gills, but too small for the rest of its body. When the fish tries to back out, its gill covers catch in the mesh and prevent its escape. Mesh sizes range from 2 inches for herring through 6 inches for salmon to 24 inches for sea turtles. The trammel net consists of three sets of webbing hung from the same corkline. The middle webbing, of small size mesh, is sandwiched between two outer webbings of

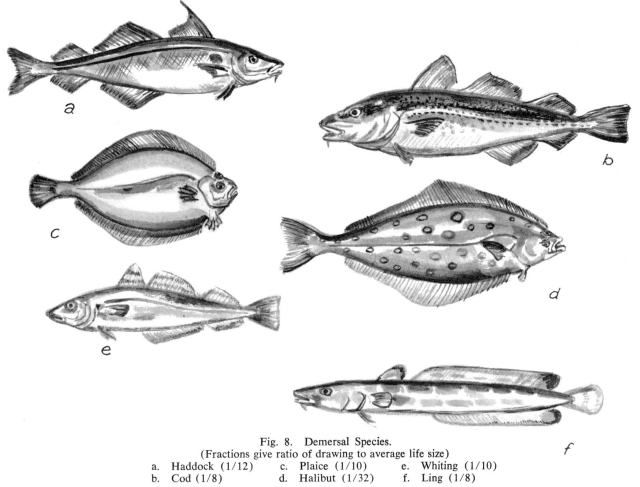

Fig. 8. Demersal Species.
(Fractions give ratio of drawing to average life size)

a. Haddock (1/12) c. Plaice (1/10) e. Whiting (1/10)
b. Cod (1/8)   d. Halibut (1/32) f. Ling (1/8)

3

larger size mesh. In a typical trammel net, these would measure about 1½ and 6 inches respectively. A fish swimming into the net passes through one coarse mesh and strikes the fine mesh. Continuing, it pushes the fine mesh through the coarse mesh on the other side, forming a pocket which traps it (fig. 9). A trammel is less selective in size of catch than the gill net. The latter takes neither small fish, which can swim through the webbing, nor large fish, whose heads are too big to enter the mesh. The trammel net catches anything that can pass through its large size outer mesh.

Both gill and trammel nets are hung from a corkline, a heavy rope bearing floats at intervals along its length. The bottom of the webbing is held down by a lead-weighted line. The mesh is made of cotton, linen, or one of the synthetic fibers: polypropylene, Nylon, Terylene, or polyvinyl chloride (PVC). Nets vary in size from single units 30 feet long and 6 feet deep to large fleets of nets, secured end to end, several miles long and several fathoms deep. If the positive buoyancy of the floats exceeds the negative buoyancy of the weights, the nets remain at the surface. Increasing the weights of the leads holds the nets at the bottom. Alternatively they can be moored in the middle waters by a combination of anchors and buoys. Less frequently they are fastened to stakes or laid in a circle around a school of fish.

Most nets are fished as pelagic drift nets—a long shallow wall of netting with its upper edge at or just below the surface (fig. 10). A single boat shoots the nets on a downwind course, then moors to the leeward end, cuts its motor, and drifts. Some boats lie bow to their nets, others stern to;

both types are called drifters. Since fish avoid the net if they can see it, drifters shoot their nets at sunset, lie to through the hours of darkness, and haul them at dawn. The bottom set net (fig. 12) lies at the sea floor. Its most common application is in fresh water fisheries and in taking king crabs.

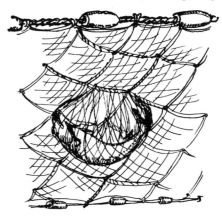

Fig. 9. Trammel Net. The trammel net consists of three walls of webbing, one of large mesh sandwiched between two of small mesh.

The most important surrounding nets are the seine and the trawl. Both types have small mesh designed to confine the fish inside the net rather than to entangle them in the webbing. Seines, also called round or ring nets, are laid around a school and the ends brought together to trap the fish. Trawls are bag-shaped nets dragged along the bottom or in midwaters with open end forward. Fish are trapped when the trawl is hauled to the surface.

4

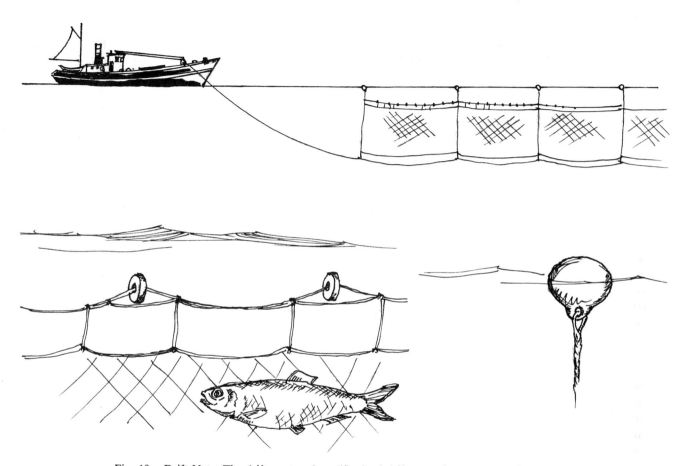

Fig. 10. Drift Net. The drifter sets a long "fleet" of drift nets, then moors to the leeward end. Floats hold the net at the proper depth; the webbing hangs between the cork line and the lead line.

5

The purse seine (fig. 14) is a large cylindrical net whose upper edge is held at the sea surface by floats strung on a corkline. At the bottom, tens or hundreds of feet below, is a lead line and, seized to it, a bridle carrying a purse ring

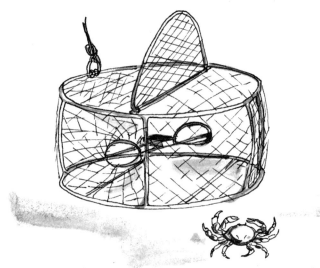

Fig. 11. Crab Trap. Crab traps are made of wire and baited with chicken heads or scrap fish. In Latin America they are called *nasas*.

every few fathoms. Through these rings runs the purse line. Hauling in the purse line closes the bottom of the seine in the same way that the drawstrings close a lady's purse. Other types of seine, such as the beach seine, the lampara, and the ring net, lack a pursing arrangement. The beach seine is hauled in shallow water where the leadline drags on the

bottom to prevent the escape of the catch. Lampara and ring net fishermen haul both top and bottom of their nets into the boat to trap the fish in the bunt. Mesh size varies; in a minnow seine it measures ¼ inch, in a herring seine 1¼ inches. The bunt, the part of the net that holds the fish after the wings have been hauled aboard, has a finer and stronger mesh than the rest of the seine. Table II gives

Table II

Type	Length (ft.)	Depth (ft.)
Scottish ring set	600	100
Italian lampara net	900	30
Mackerel purse seine	1500	30
North Sea herring seine	1500	450
Puget Sound drum seine	1800	66
Canadian tuna seine	4000	400
Japanese purse seine	8500	1000

dimensions of seven typical seines. The deeper and heavier nets allow seiners to fish the middle waters inaccessible to drifters and bottom trawlers alike.

Seiners handle their nets in different ways. The seine can be set directly by the seiner or by supporting seine skiffs. Hauling was originally a hand operation requiring a large crew and one or more skiffs to assist. Power blocks (fig. 13) were developed to facilitate handling and permit the use of larger nets. The blocks are sometimes mounted on the skiffs, sometimes on the seiner itself. The latter arrangement, by eliminating the small boats, reduces crew size and labor costs

6

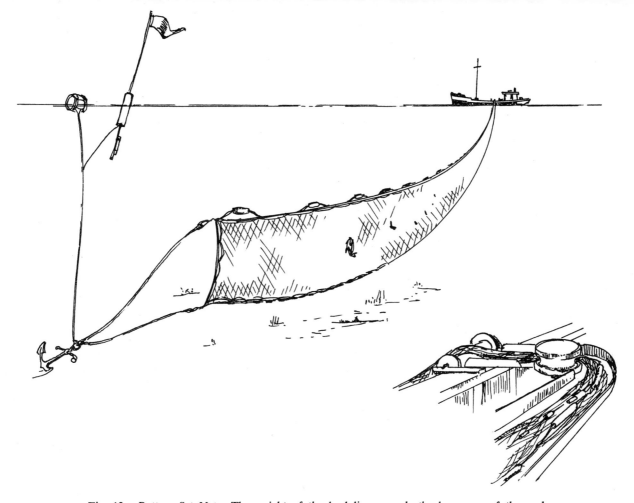

Fig. 12. Bottom Set Net. The weight of the lead line exceeds the buoyancy of the cork line, and the net remains at the bottom. A powered net winder at the deck edge facilitates hauling the heavy net and catch.

7

and allows operations on the high seas. On the other hand it involves a large and expensive power source and possibly a decrease in stability. The drag of hauling a seine makes conventionally powered craft unmaneuverable. There is a constant danger of the net fouling in the propeller with serious damage to both. The newest seiners avoid this problem by the use of thrusters. These are small propellers

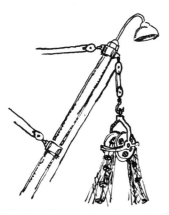

Fig. 13. Power Block. Purse seines have become too large for efficient handling by manpower. Modern seiners haul their net with a power block at the boom end.

mounted in athwartships ducts below the water line at one or both ends of the ship. They produce a lateral thrust counteracting the drag of hauling the seine. By adjusting thruster speed the skipper can control the heading of his boat, keeping the screw clear and maintaining proper aspect to wind and sea.

The term *trawler*, in an unfortunate exception to the mariner's traditionally precise vocabulary, has become a synonym for fishing boat. Only those craft which drag trawl nets should rightly be called trawlers. Others should be given the name descriptive of their gear; doryman, seiner, drifter, etc. Figure 16 shows a typical otter trawl. It is made up of twelve or more separate sections of webbing laced together by hand. The mesh is of natural fiber, which is cheaper, or synthetic fiber, which is lighter and stronger. The trawl tapers from a wide mouth to a long narrow cod end. The mouth is held open in the horizontal plane by otter boards which spread the wings of the trawl. The mouth is kept open in the vertical plane by floats of glass, steel, aluminum, cork, or plastic strung along the corkline and by weights secured to the lead line. Wooden or rubber rollers may also be strung on the lead line to protect the trawl on rough bottoms. The trawl ends in a narrow cylindrical bag, the cod end, which holds the catch. When the trawl has been swung on deck the cod end line is untied to dump the fish.

The beam trawl (fig. 18) is similar to the otter trawl except that the wings are spread by a horizontal spar or beam. Handling problems limit the length of the beam and make the beam trawl smaller than the otter trawl. The dredge, similar to the beam trawl but still smaller, has a net of heavy line or chain (fig. 17). It is used for taking scallops, oysters, clams, and other shellfish.

Ground fish trawls are weighted to run along the bottom. Fish-finding sonar has made it possible to find shoals of

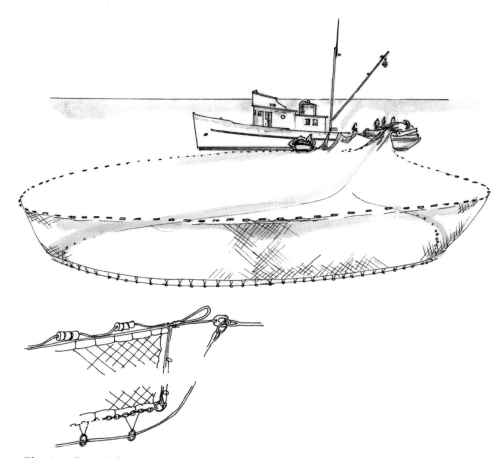

Fig. 14. Purse Seine. In this sketch a mackerel seiner has completed setting the seine and is ready to "purse" and haul it. The seine is stowed on a rotating platform on the fantail.

fish in the midwaters between surface and bottom. To catch these fish, midwater or pelagic trawls have been developed to run at a set depth below the surface. Trawl depth is controlled by varying the boat's speed; depth is measured either by calculation from angle and length of trawl warp, by net-mounted sonar transducer, or by telemetry from a net-mounted pressure gage. Like the deep purse seine the mid-

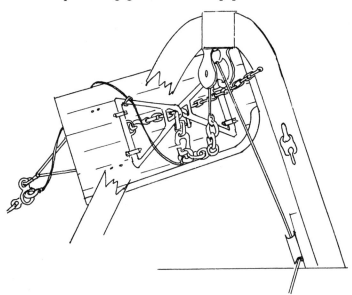

Fig. 15. Gallows and Otter Board. When a side trawl is hauled, the otter boards are chained to the gallows while the net is hauled on board. Iron "runners" or "shoes" on the lower edge of the board prevent damage from rocks on the sea bottom.

water trawl is opening valuable new fisheries in the middle layers of the sea.

Traditionally trawls have been towed by warps led over the side of the trawler through a pair of blocks, one forward and one aft. The blocks hang from gallows, inverted U-shaped structures characteristic of the trawler. Towing and recovering the trawl over the stern, however, has proven simpler, safer, and cheaper. Stern trawlers are now being built in all sizes from the largest to the smallest. Another innovation is the double-rigged shrimp boat, towing a trawl from each of its two outriggers. In pair trawling, two boats combine forces to drag a larger trawl than either could handle alone. Otter boards are unnecessary; the separation of the two boats holds the trawl wings open. Similar to a trawl but handled differently is the Danish seine net. Instead of towing his net, the seiner shoots the seine, pays out about a mile of warp, and then hauls it in while lying to.

Table III gives dimensions of seven different trawls and illustrates the variety of shapes and sizes.

Hook and line take both pelagic and demersal species. The longline, as its name suggests, measures up to 20 miles in length, with hooks fastened every few fathoms (fig. 20). Each end is anchored and buoyed. The line is fished on the bottom for taking ground fish in areas where the sea bed is too rough for trawling. In the shark and tuna fisheries, floats keep the baits near the surface. Small boats tend long lines by hand, coiling them in tubs. Larger craft are fitted with a gurdy or mechanical line hauler and a power driven drum to stow the heavy ¼ inch diameter line.

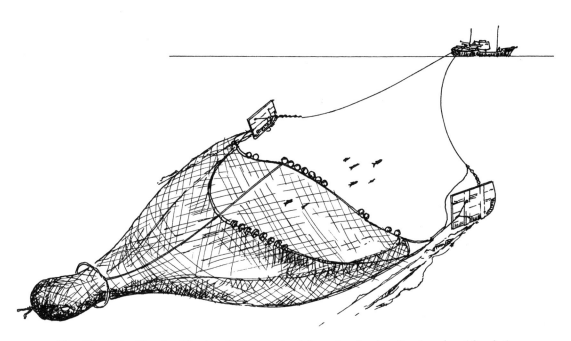

Fig. 16. Otter Trawl. The trawl warps extend from trawler to otter boards. Aft of the boards the ground wire leads via a heavy shackle or Dan Leno scuttle to the head rope and foot rope. To these are laced the wings and mouth of the trawl. The splitting strap, encircling the cod end, is used to lift the catch on board.

11

Another method of taking pelagic fish is by trolling a lure or baited hook astern. Usually a small boat, the troller mounts outriggers to handle a number of lines. He may have a gurdy to assist in hauling in the catch. Tuna clippers also use hook and line. The clipper lures a school of tuna close alongside by chumming with live bait fish. The fishing rig is a large baitless hook or jig secured by stout lines to

Table III

	Width (ft.)	Depth (ft.)	Length (ft.)	Doors
Chesapeake oyster dredge	8	4	8	--
Australian inshore trawl	20	5	55	2' × 3'
Baltic midwater pair trawl	25	25	138	--
Beam trawl	40	6	80	--
Gulf coast flat shrimp trawl	40	8	50	2' × 5'
Iceland trawl	100	20	150	4' × 8'
Danish seine net	150	10	75	--

two or three poles, one man handling each pole (fig. 19). The tuna strike the hooks readily and the fisherman swings them on deck.

In the world's less developed areas bottom fishing with individual hook and line is an important method. It calls for the simplest and cheapest of gear and is adapted to boats of every shape and kind. Sometimes a number of hooks are fastened to a single line so as to fish at different depths. Large boats fish a number of lines, tending them by hand. Fish or shellfish are used for bait.

Impaling gear includes the harpoon (fig. 89) and in primitive fisheries the bow and arrow or gig. Swordfishermen still throw the harpoon by hand, but whalers have adopted the harpoon gun. The whale catcher is a specialized high-speed craft built to locate and harpoon whales. Other boats recover the carcasses and tow them to the factory ship.

In shallow coastal waters pound nets are fastened to stakes to form fish traps (fig. 22). Funnel shaped arrangements

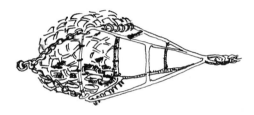

Fig. 17. Dredge. Smaller and heavier than a trawl, the dredge has metal frames and a webbing of heavy rope or wire. Heavy weight helps it dig shellfish from the sea bottom.

lead the fish into a meshed enclosure or pound from which they cannot escape. Small boats remove the catch. Shellfish and some species of fish are taken in bottom traps of various designs including lobster pots, crab traps, and fish pots or *nasas* (figs. 6 and 11). The pots are buoyed for recovery by small boats. Boatmen use oyster tongs (fig. 21) to scoop oysters from the bottom in shallow waters.

Advances in electronics have given the fishing fleet valuable equipment for communications, navigation, and fish-finding. Radiotelephone is found on board most fishermen

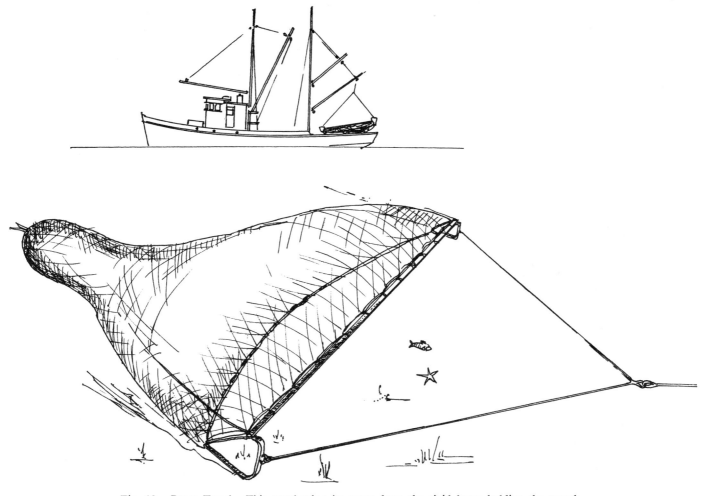

Fig. 18. Beam Trawl. This trawl takes its name from the rigid beam holding the mouth open. Otter boards are not required, but the length and weight of the beam limit it to relatively small size.

13

today, not only as a safety measure but also as an essential element in fishing methods. Factory and mother ships control their catcher boats by radiotelephone. Tuna clippers and purse seiners use aircraft to locate fish and radio their location to the boats. Weather broadcasts, storm warnings, and distress messages help make safer an inherently dangerous business.

Fig. 19. Tuna Hook and Line. Tuna clippers attract their catch with live bait, then drop bare hooks into the feeding school. Tuna, striking readily, are hooked and swung aboard. Their large size requires heavy gear and two or three men to each hook.

Compact, navigational aids with low power input are commonplace. Radar, Decca, loran, and radio direction finder (R.D.F.) are standard equipment on all but the smallest craft (fig. 23). Besides conventional navigation, they allow the skipper to plot the positions of schools of fish located by his fish-finder, and to avoid net damage by pinpointing wrecks, snags, and rough bottom areas.

Fish-finders are high frequency sonars for locating schools of fish. Utilizing sonic echo ranging, the transducer emits a powerful pulse of underwater sound. It receives echoes from the bottom, from other ships, from schools of fish, and from any other underwater reflecting body. The set measures the time between outgoing pulse and returning echo and converts it to distance from ship to fish. The simplest fish-finders, called echo sounders, point straight downward beneath the keel (fig. 107). They indicate water depth as well as the presence of fish directly under the boat. Scanning fish-finders or sonars send their signals all around the ship to determine range and bearing of schools in any direction.

Fishery research is applying modern technology to fishing methods, and novel approaches are under investigation in several countries. Lights are being used to attract fish, magnetic and electric fields to control their movement, and pumps to take them aboard. By the close of the century hooks and nets may have given way to electronic fish catchers. These, together with automated processing and freezing equipment, could revolutionize commercial fishing by increasing catches and reducing crew size.

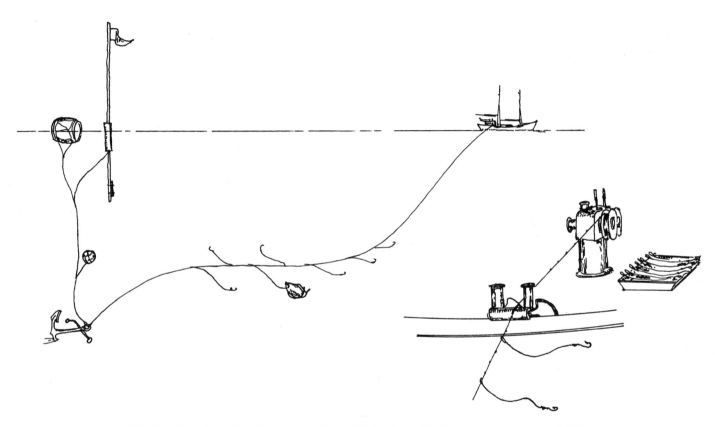

Fig. 20. Longline. Longlines can be buoyed for pelagic fish (fig. 60) or set on the bottom for demersal species. Small boats haul the line by hand; larger draft vessels utilize a powered line hauler or "gurdy."

15

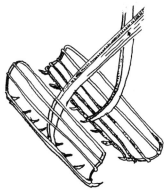

Fig. 21. Oyster Tongs. Chesapeake Bay watermen tong oysters in depths up to twenty feet.

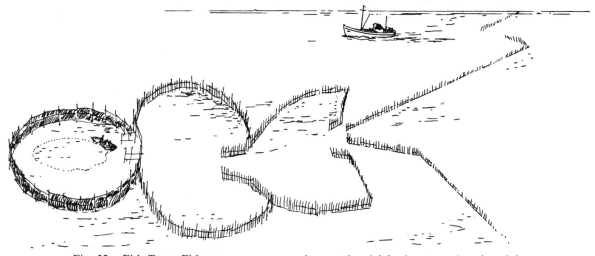

Fig. 22. Fish Trap. Fish traps are numerous in coastal and inland waters. A series of funnel shaped nets lead the catch into the "pound," where small boats scoop them on board. Fishermen take their nets ashore during certain seasons; the stakes remain throughout the year.

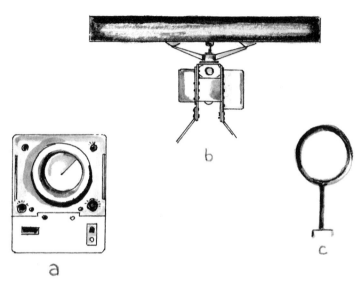

Fig. 23. Radar and Radio Direction Finder. Radar, an electronic aid to navigation, displays range and bearing of land, ships, and navigational aids. These appear as light colored "pips" on the dark surface of a cathode ray tube (a). The antenna (b), mounted topside, rotates continuously in dark or foggy weather. A loop antenna (c) connected to a radio direction finder (R.D.F.) gives bearings of radio beacons.

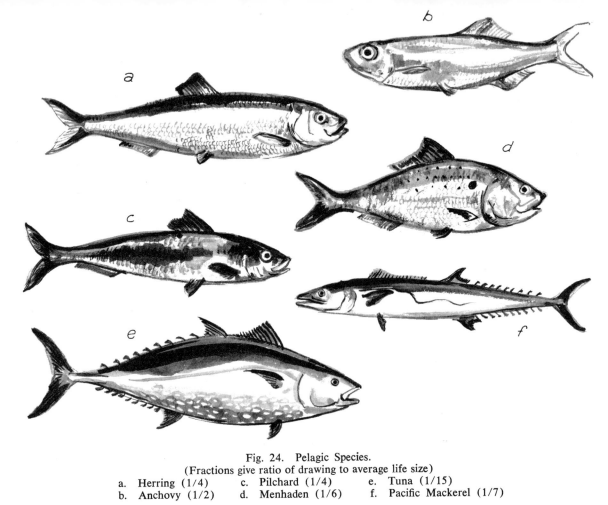

Fig. 24. Pelagic Species.
(Fractions give ratio of drawing to average life size)

a. Herring (1/4)   c. Pilchard (1/4)   e. Tuna (1/15)
b. Anchovy (1/2)   d. Menhaden (1/6)   f. Pacific Mackerel (1/7)

II. Trawlers

Trawlers vary in size and shapes; in size because of trawl dimensions and fish hold capacity, in shape because of different methods of handling the trawl. Trawl size ranges from 8 to 150 feet, and trawler lengths vary proportionally, from 30 to 300 feet with a few 400-footers. Hold capacities vary from hundreds of pounds to hundreds of tons. There are three arrangements of trawl gear—stern, side, and outrigger—each lending a characteristic appearance to the ship (fig. 27).

The side trawler's fish deck is forward, his winch amidships. From the winch trawl warps run, one forward and one aft, to blocks at the deck edge. Each block hangs from a gallows (fig. 15), a conspicuous A-frame characteristic of the side trawler. Thence the warps lead aft through a hookup block on the quarter to the otter boards and trawl. Figure 27d is a coastal dragger, figure 27f a modern middle-water trawler, figure 29 a distant-water trawler.

The stern trawler shoots, tows, and hauls his gear over the stern. From the winch one warp goes aft on each side of the ship, over the quarter by way of a swivel block, then to the otter board and trawl. When the net is hauled, the winch pulls in the wings and a stern gantry swings the cod end up a ramp to the fish deck. The modern stern trawlers make fish-ing safer and more economical, and for those reasons may replace the side trawler. Figures 5 and 27a are large fish-factory stern trawlers. Figure 27c is an inshore craft.

Shrimp trawlers tow each trawl from a single warp connected by a bridle to its two otter boards. Most shrimpers are double-rigged to tow two trawls. One warp passes from the winch to the end of an outrigger or towing boom on the port side; the other to a similar arrangement to starboard. Small size and prominent outriggers identify the shrimper (fig. 27e).

Fig. 25. Inshore Trawlers. Small stern trawlers from Barcelona, Valencia, Cartagena, and Cadiz fish Spanish inshore waters. Their brightly painted hulls are marked by a high bow and an overhanging counter.

Sailing trawlers are common in the Far East, and a few remain in Europe and America. Figure 27b is a Brixham trawler from the English Channel; figure 26 a Chesapeake oyster dredger.

Inshore trawlers land their catches daily while larger craft ice the catch or refrigerate it. Middle and distant water trawlers store their fish whole or gutted but otherwise unprocessed. Their catch is processed ashore before sale to the consumer. Fish factory trawlers are equipped to fillet the catch, freeze the fillets, produce fish meal, extract fish oil, or cook and can the catch. Their product is ready for sale as soon as the boat ties up.

DEEP SEA SIDE TRAWLERS

The backbone of many distant-water fishing fleets is the deep sea side trawler. Typical of this type is the Polish built B-20 trawler (fig. 29). One of the world's largest builders of fishing vessels, Poland controls its worldwide ship sales through Centromor, the government import-export office for shipbuilding. Centromor has sold B-20's to Britain, France, and in large quantities to Russia. A modern and efficient freezer trawler, the B-20 measures 200 feet overall and grosses about 900 tons. She is fast, 13 to 14 knots, and can stay at sea for 45 days. The engine room holds either one large or two smaller diesels, depending on the design. Some plants drive a constant pitch propeller; others a variable pitch. Centralized on the bridge are the electronic navigation aids and the ship and fishing gear controls. The B-21, Centromor's smaller distant-water trawler, has also

found a ready market. Polish shipbuilders deliver a portion of their output to their own fleet as it expands from the Baltic into the North Sea and Atlantic fisheries.

East German yards produce the 167 foot *Okean* class trawler, one of the most numerous in the Soviet fleet.

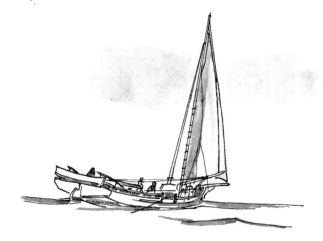

Fig. 26. Skipjack. A traditional Chesapeake design, the skipjack has a shallow draft V-bottom and a centerboard. The large, heavy mainsail is usually jib-headed. The yawl boat is carried astern on davits.

A standard distant-water craft, the *Okeans* gross 500 tons. Lacking refrigeration, they ice their catch and normally deliver it to mother ships. Although relatively new, the *Okeans* are being replaced in the Russian Atlantic and Far East fleets by larger vessels. Like Poland, East Germany is building for its own fleet and taking to the high seas.

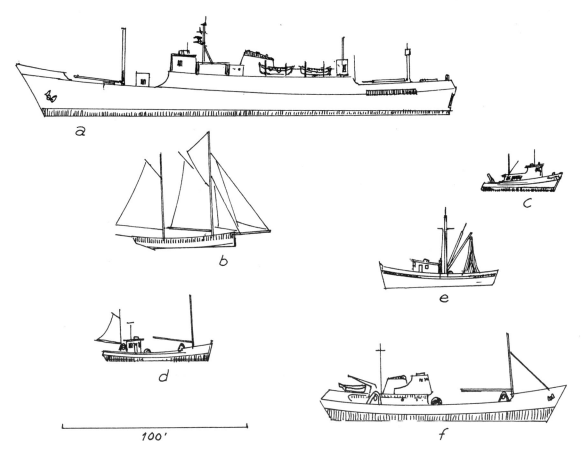

100'

Fig. 27. Trawlers.

a. Fish-factory Stern Trawler   d. Dragger
b. Brixham Trawler   e. Shrimper
c. Inshore Stern Trawler   f. Middle-water Side Trawler

21

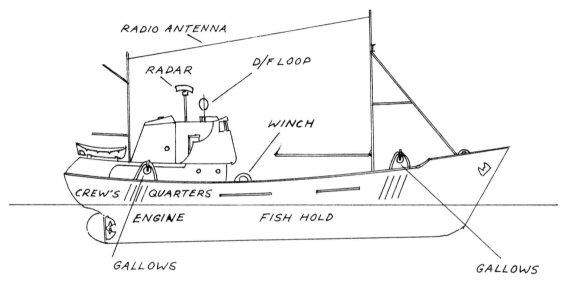

RADIO ANTENNA

RADAR

D/F LOOP

WINCH

CREW'S //// QUARTERS

ENGINE   FISH HOLD

GALLOWS

GALLOWS

Fig. 28. Parts of a Trawler. This craft is a small European side trawler with engine and deckhouse aft. The bulwark is clear of any fittings between the gallows which might foul the trawl net or warps.

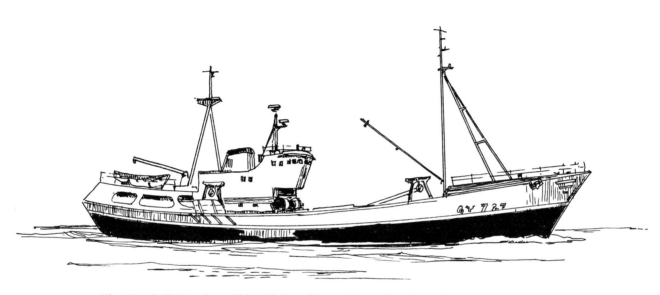

Fig. 29. B-20 Trawler. This 200-foot side trawler typifies the modern craft coming from Polish shipyards. Fast and well equipped, she can cruise in distant waters for 45 days.

Japan, whose annual catch is the largest in the world after Peru's, operates trawler fleets in every ocean. Trawlers comprise a large part of the 700 Japanese vessels that annually fish off the west coasts of Canada and the United States. Most work as catcher boats, transferring their fish to mother ships for freezing or reduction to fish meal. A typical craft measures 175 feet overall with a high flaring bow, fish deck amidships, and engine aft. Its catch consists of flatfish, cod, sablefish, and ocean perch.

On the Grand Banks of Newfoundland the Soviet-bloc fleet is joined by trawlers from France, Spain and Portugal. British distant-water trawlers prefer the northern grounds of Iceland, Spitzbergen, Bear Island, and in the Barents and White Seas. The United States lacks distant-water trawlers; its largest measure just over 100 feet and operate in waters near home port.

MIDDLE-WATER TRAWLERS

The British trawler fleet comprises distant-water, middle-water, and inshore or near-water vessels. For the British, middle waters extend from the North Sea to the Faroes. The English boats operate chiefly from Hull, Grimsby, Lowestoft, and Fleetwood; Welsh boats from Milford Haven; and Scottish boats from Aberdeen and the Firth of Forth.

Admiral Drake (fig. 31) is one of the newest middle-water trawlers. As her bow designator indicates, she operates from Aberdeen, where she was built. Measuring 128 feet overall, she is diesel propelled at a service speed of 12 knots.

A high forecastle and marked sheer help protect the fish deck amidships. Unlike smaller "one-sided" boats, she has gallows port and starboard. Rubbing strips below the gallows prevent damage to the sides from otter boards and other heavy trawl gear. Just forward of the bridge is the rugged trawl winch for handling the warps. Its diesel electric drive

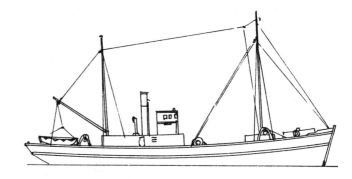

Fig. 30. Steam Trawler. Although modern craft are diesel driven, a few steam trawlers still fish in European waters. Compare the tall thin funnel to the low, streamlined stack of the B-20 in figure 29. Distant-water steam trawlers leave port with their decks full of coal to take them to the grounds.

is powerful enough to overcome the thousands of pounds towing drag at trawling speed. A typical cruise takes *Admiral Drake* to the Faroes, 300 miles northwest of Aberdeen, and keeps her at sea for two weeks. With luck she might bring in a top catch of whitefish weighing 1000 "kits" (about 75 tons) selling for £5000 ($14,000).

Fig. 31. Middle-water Trawler. British middle-water trawlers fish on the high seas as far north as Iceland. Their cruises last two to three weeks. This 128 foot diesel craft is rigged to trawl on either side. The raised forecastle helps protect the fish deck from high seas.

Older trawlers are steam propelled with a thin stack and a steadying sail on the mizzen (fig. 30). In recent construction steam has given way to diesel or, in some of the largest, diesel electric propulsion. The traditional fixed pitch propeller is slowly yielding to the controllable pitch screw because of the latter's operational flexibility and simplification of machinery design. Another innovation is the integration of ship control for maximum efficiency. From a single console in the pilothouse the skipper can conn the ship, navigate, and control fishing operations.

Like other trawlers *Admiral Drake* burns a white stern light and red and green side lights. In addition she is required to carry trawling lights at the masthead: all-round green over all-round white. By day she hoists the fisherman's mark of a pair of black cones point-to-point. Smaller trawlers are permitted to substitute a fish basket for the cones.

DRAGGERS

On the continental shelf of eastern North America lie some of the world's richest fisheries. Extending from Labrador to Cape Hatteras, they include the well-known Georges Bank off Cape Cod and Newfoundland's Grand Banks. To fish these grounds European countries have built large craft with long endurance. American and Canadian fishermen, having only a short run to the grounds, have developed a smaller craft—the dragger. Basically a New England design, the dragger's year-round catches of flounder, haddock, ocean perch, scallops, and cod rank New Bedford and Boston among the country's leading fishing ports. Since the 1930's

draggers have also worked farther south, and a fleet of fifty boats now fish out of Hampton Roads.

Small wooden craft ranging from 60 to 125 feet overall, draggers step two masts with a small steadying sail. The

Fig. 32.   Canadian Dragger. This modern diesel trawler carries gallows fore and aft for side trawling. Larger than the New England craft in figure 33, she can make longer cruises and handle a larger catch.

deckhouse is aft and the winch just forward of the house. In the engine room is a powerful diesel to tow the heavy trawl or dredges. For catching ground fish they are rigged as side trawlers with gallows fore and aft, usually on one side only. Figure 33 shows a small New England boat; figure 32 a larger and newer Canadian. For scalloping they are rigged

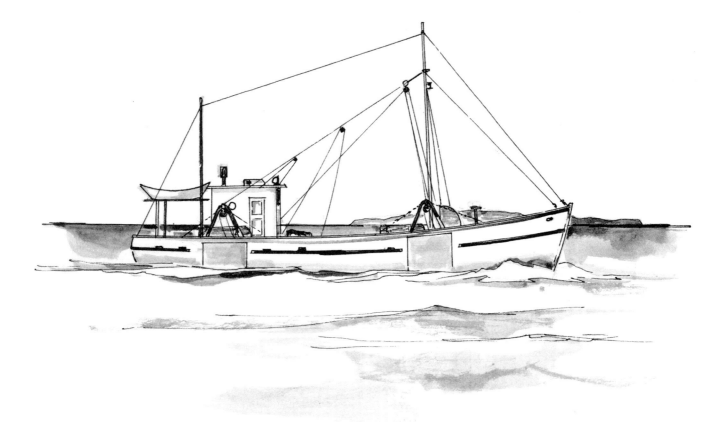

Fig. 33. New England Dragger. Boats of this type fish from Maine to the Virginia Capes. In 1964 a fleet of almost 1000 draggers landed 685,000,000 pounds of fish from these waters. Despite their small size (averaging about 50 to 60 tons gross), they operate year-round to produce about one quarter of the annual U.S. catch.

as dredgers with gallows forward only, port and starboard (frontispiece). The scalloper's foremast mounts a pair of booms to handle the two dredges. One or two small boats are carried in quarter davits or on top of the deckhouse.

Fig. 34. French Inshore Trawler *La Marie Lise*. Her silhouette, with flush deck and after deck house, resembles that of the New England dragger on the opposite side of the North Atlantic. Propelled by a 300 horsepower diesel, she is rigged to trawl from the starboard side only.

The crew of six to eight spends about a week at sea. Transits are short and most of the cruise is spent on the grounds.

The trawler shoots his trawl, drags it several hours, then hauls it on board. The catch is dumped on deck, washed down to clean off the mud, then sorted by size and species. Some are gutted before icing; others are iced down "in the round." The dredger empties his scallops on deck where they are shucked by a fisherman with a knife. The adductor or "eye" is removed, washed, bagged, and iced down. The rest of the scallop is thrown overboard. Research has shown that refrigeration preserves fish better than ice, but most draggers are too small for a large and expensive refrigeration plant.

INSHORE TRAWLERS

Various modifications of the trawl are used in near water or inshore fisheries. The bull trawl or pair trawl is a large net towed by two boats fitted with winches and sometimes quarter gallows. From each craft a single warp leads to a bridle secured to one wing of the trawl. Steaming on parallel courses, the boats regulate the spread of the wings by steering closer together or farther apart. Weights on the lead line and floats on the corkline keep the mouth open and give overall negative buoyancy. By changing their speed the boats keep the trawl at the proper depth for the fish they are seeking. Their combined power allows two boats to handle a much bigger trawl than either could alone, and their maneuverability simplifies control of depth and spread. In the Baltic, for example, Finnish herring boats of 15 to 20 horsepower tow midwater trawls 135 feet long with a 20 by 20 foot mouth.

Fig. 35.　Motor Fishing Vessel.　The seine, which requires less power than the otter trawl, is fished from small craft like this m.f.v.　Double ended and clinker built, her design is typically British.　She carries a buoy forward to mark good fishing grounds.

Another rig used inshore is the seine net. Resembling an otter trawl without doors, a typical net measures 200 feet across by 10 feet high with a cod end 100 feet long. The seiner lays an anchor or buoy to which he secures one warp. He then steams downwind or downcurrent paying out the warp. With the warp laid, the seiner turns across current and shoots the net. Then he steers upcurrent and streams the second warp as he returns to the starting point to take the first warp on board. The seiner may anchor or he may steam slowly ahead as he hauls in the warps and brings the seine on board. Developed in Denmark, this rig is often called the Danish seine. It is used the world over—by German luggers, by British m.f.v.'s (figs. 1 and 35), by Australian small craft, and by Japanese sampans. The typical seiner measures up to 60 feet with a 200 horsepower diesel.

Side set trawls and stern trawls are also common in near waters, the former in Northern Europe and the latter in the Mediterranean. Figure 34 shows a small French trawler. Some are even smaller: a 30 foot launch can tow and recover a trawl measuring 60 feet across with three-foot otter boards. Figures 2 and 25 show stern trawlers from Spain and Italy. Shellfish are taken by dredge; figure 121 shows a Dutch inshore mussel boat. Her warps are streamed from towing booms rather than gallows. Otherwise she resembles the New England scalloper, her counterpart across the Atlantic.

NORTH SEA TRAWLERS

Europe's most important fishing ground is the North Sea (fig. 37). Near the Norwegian coast the bottom lies below 100 fathoms. Steaming south one enters shallower water and crosses the ten fathom curve before leaving the North Sea through the Straits of Dover. The average sounding is 30 fathoms. These shallow fertile waters have traditionally supported a drift net fishery for herring and a trawl fishery for whitefish, but recent years have seen a dwindling catch for

Fig. 36. Midwater Trawler. Pelagic trawlers are replacing drifters in the North Sea herring fishery. *G. M. Daneker,* the boat shown here, has twice made the largest annual catch in the German fleet.

the drifters. Led by the Norwegians, the North Sea herring fleet has increasingly turned to the purse seine and the pelagic or midwater trawl. Today trawlers from Norway, Britain, Holland, Belgium, France, Denmark, and West Germany share the grounds with long range craft from the Baltic countries.

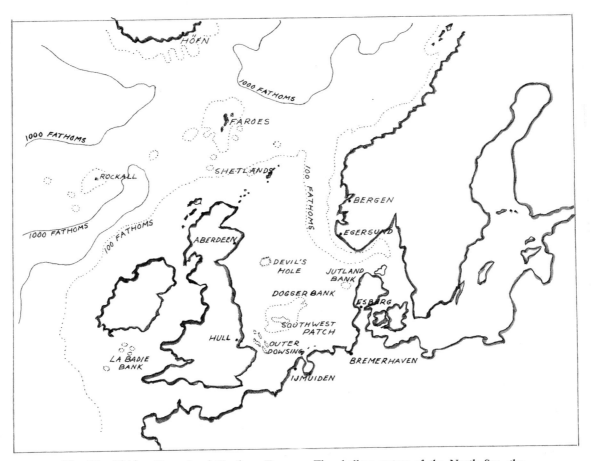

Fig. 37. Fishing Grounds of Northern Europe. The shallow waters of the North Sea, the Baltic, and the southern Norwegian Sea support some of the world's richest fisheries. This chart shows important banks and fishing ports.

Whitefish boats are conventional side trawlers or, in increasing numbers, stern trawlers. For the herring fishery a new type of vessel designed for pelagic trawling is coming off the ways. Some are rigged only for midwater trawling; others can fish a variety of gear. Figure 36 shows a German boat designed for pelagic side trawling. Trawlers from the Baltic often work with freezer transport ships who carry the catch to port while the trawlers continue to work on the grounds.

Britain, with many craft too small to handle a large pelagic trawl, is adopting the Swedish system of pair trawling. Design and operation of a small midwater trawl for single boat towing has proven difficult. It is hard to keep the wings spread and to regulate the depth. Two boats steaming on parallel course, on the other hand, can easily keep the wings open. Their combined power is enough to maintain trawl speed and depth. *Girl Jane* is a new Scottish craft designed for pair trawling. A 63 foot, 200 horsepower combination boat, she can also convert to drifting or seining. For large craft to replace the vanishing drifter, it remains to be seen whether Britain will turn to the purse seiner or to the pelagic trawler.

LARGE STERN TRAWLERS

The largest of all fish catching vessels is the factory stern trawler. Since her processing and stowage capacity are proportional to her catching ability, she can make economically feasible trips to distant grounds without support ships. Developed in Europe in the last decade, this type vessel is growing in numbers and in size. The biggest is the 423 foot

Natalia Kovshova. Built in France for the U.S.S.R., she grosses 8425 tons—as big as a Liberty ship. Also new but smaller is the East German built *Atlantik* class (fig. 39). A development of the successful *Tropik* factory trawler, she measures 270 feet overall with a 44 foot beam and a gross tonnage in the vicinity of 2500. A superstructure set well forward and an unusual side-by-side stack arrangement per-

Fig. 38. *Victory*. Operating from Grimsby, *Victory* is designed for Iceland, Bear Island, and other distant grounds. The catch is frozen on board and offloaded in frozen blocks to cold storage plants ashore. Stern trawling, freezing, diesel electric drive, and roll stabilization are successful innovations in the British trawler fleet.

mit a long broad trawl deck. The after gantry and the square stern with inclined slipway are characteristic of this type. Twin diesels coupled to a variable pitch propeller provide 2600 horsepower for a cruising speed of 13 knots. Auxiliary equipment includes trawl winch, line haulers, refrigeration system, and hydraulically operated deck hatches. The processing machinery turns out frozen blocks, meal and oil. Fish-finding sonar, multichannel V.H.F. radio, and an active rudder are fitted. The rudder pivots 90 degrees in either

Fig. 39. *Atlantik* Class Stern Trawler. A modern East German design, the *Atlantik* class trawlers are built for 60-day voyages in warm or cold waters. Special attention has been given to crew comfort: air conditioning, two and four berth cabins, and even a sauna bath. *Atlantik* will be able to trawl midwaters or on the bottom, and the catch can be frozen or processed into fish meal.

direction and mounts a ducted propeller driven by a 70 kilowatt motor to produce side thrust for low-speed maneuverability.

Polish shipyards are producing similar vessels ranging in size from the 230 foot B-23 class to the 280 foot B-18's. Japan has built stern trawlers up to 300 feet, 3500 gross tons, both for export and for her own fleet. Britain's newest stern trawlers are typified by *Cape Kennedy* (fig. 5) and *Victory* (fig. 38). *Victory's* dimensions are comparable to *Atlantik's* : length 245 feet, beam 41 feet, propulsion 2700 horsepower. She displays the characteristic stern gantry and slipway. *Victory's* three-engine diesel electric power plant is an innovation and she is the first British trawler to be fitted with roll stabilizing tanks. Modern processing equipment includes washers, freezers, conveyors, and special arrangements for mechanical offloading of the catch. Her fish room holds 450 tons of frozen fish at 20° Fahrenheit.

MEDIUM STERN TRAWLERS

The stern trawling principle has been applied to medium and small craft as well as to the large factory trawlers. Medium-sized vessels measuring 100 to 200 feet, with their high bows and square sterns, present an unusual silhouette. In contrast to the side trawlers, the stern trawler has its deckhouse and superstructure well forward. This arrangement facilitates hauling the trawl on board and provides protection for winchmen and net handlers. The fish deck is almost completely enclosed. Like the fish factories, most medium stern trawlers are refrigerated. Smaller size prevents the installation of complete processing equipment. A fixed or swinging stern gantry or a pair of gallows on the quarters are characteristic. Sometimes the engine exhaust is led topside through side-by-side funnels to permit an unbroken fish deck. Both bottom and midwater trawls are used, particularly in

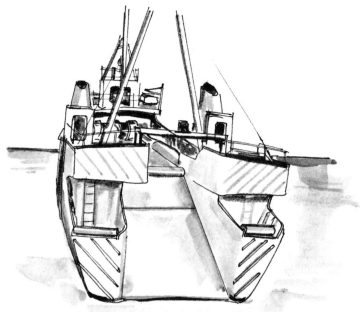

Fig. 40. Slipway of **Medium Stern Trawler**. The stern trawl is spreading to New England and the Maritime Provinces. *Brandal*, shown here, was built in Halifax in 1965. Her design features maximum protection of work areas.

Fig. 41. *Rijnmond I.* This 478 ton Dutch trawler shows a distinctive silhouette. She has a sharply raking bow and her bridge and funnel are amidships rather than forward as in other stern trawlers. The gantry at the stern is of British design. *Rijnmond* is 140 feet long, has a beam of 28 feet, and draws 13 feet.

the North Sea herring fishery. Frequently these craft are designed as dual purpose vessels able to shift to other fishing methods with minimum change in equipment. Trawler-longliner and trawler-seiner combinations make the change by fitting line haulers or power blocks respectively.

Fig. 42. Drum Trawler. Trawlers on the U.S. Pacific Coast fish their net astern. In drum trawling, a recent innovation, the net is recovered by reeling on a drum rather than by hoisting it overhead with a boom. The drum operation is faster, safer, and requires less manpower.

Figure 40 shows the stern slipway of a 135 foot Canadian trawler. She has a typical gantry and port and starboard stacks. Diesel propelled at 12 knots, she can carry 200 tons of iced fish. *Rijnmond I* (fig. 41) is the first of a class of Dutch stern trawlers. She is 140 feet long with a 1300 horsepower diesel. Her pivoted gantry or "Unigan" is hydraulically operated. After bringing in the otter boards, it swings the cod end of the trawl over the transom and then forward to the fish hatches. A new Norwegian stern trawler-longliner, *Andenesfiske*, is 116 feet long. She has a 13-man crew and is powered by a 750 horsepower diesel. *Ross Fame*, prototype of a British class, is 120 feet in length with 950 horsepower and a 10-man crew. Similar craft fish from France, Germany, Norway, and South Africa. Faster and easier net handling, greater safety in rough weather, and smaller crew make the medium stern trawler a serious competitor to the traditional side trawler.

SMALL STERN TRAWLERS

Small trawlers in the Mediterranean and on the Pacific coast of the United States have traditionally towed their nets over the stern. In the past decade the stern trawl, improved and automated, has become a feature of trawler design in fisheries formerly dominated by the side trawl. Like their larger sisters most small stern trawlers are marked by a forward deckhouse, unobstructed after deck, winch amidships or even slightly forward, A-frame or gallows on the quarters, and a broad overhanging stern to keep the trawl out of the propeller. Taken together these design features make for smaller crews and easier, safer operation—impor-

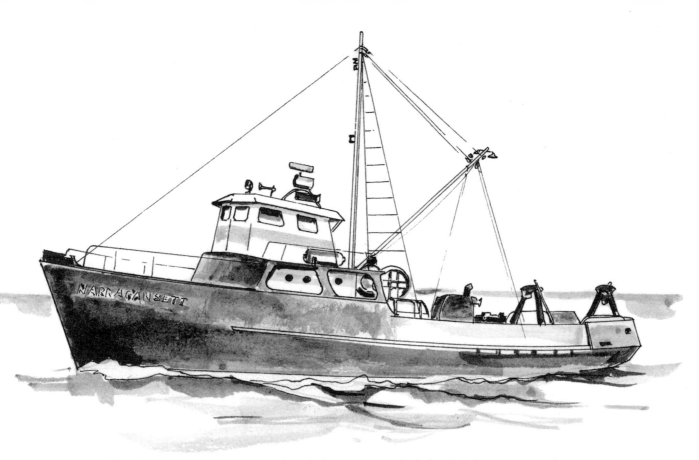

Fig. 43. *Narragansett*. New England built, *Narragansett's* design includes many new features: stern trawl, steel hull, automated gear, controllable pitch propeller, modern electronic installation. Eighty-three feet overall, she draws 9 feet. The engine is mounted all the way aft, directly over the short propeller shaft which it drives by a gear belt. Rated as 385 horsepower, the diesel drives her at 11 knots. *Narragansett* can change her rig from trawl to purse seine or scallop dredge.

tant economic factors in a period when labor costs are rising and the seagoing life becoming less popular.

Figure 42 shows the stern of an American Pacific coast drum trawler. The gallows support trawl warp blocks and hold the otter boards. Besides stowing the trawl when not in use, the drum is power driven to pay out while shooting and to reel in when hauling. A boom and whip hoist the cod

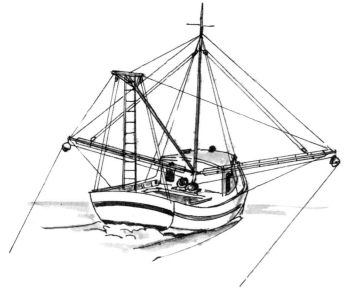

Fig. 44. Double-rigged Shrimp Boat. This shrimper carries typical Gulf rig: outriggers port and starboard, main boom rigidly fixed amidships, and ladder to boom head. Four trawl doors are used, two on each side.

end over the gunwale with the catch. *Narragansett* (fig. 43) is one of the first stern trawlers on the Atlantic coast. She too winds her trawl on a drum. Located nearly amidships, it drags the cod end up a slipway, a safer and simpler procedure than swinging it aboard with a boom. Other innovations are a controllable pitch propeller, automatic steering, and a centralized control console in the trawl cab overlooking the fish deck. The South African trawler in figure 3 is similar in design to *Narragansett* but, at 65 feet overall, slightly smaller. Some craft of this type have been built in South African yards, others imported from the United Kingdom.

In Britain the traditional double-ended motor fishing vessel with deckhouse aft is being challenged by the small combination boat with transom stern and forward deckhouse. Fitted primarily for stern trawling, it can be easily modified to fish with seine nets or longlines. Emphasis is laid on navigational equipment and laborsaving devices to make the operation economical and efficient. Even a 47-footer may be fitted with automatic pilot, radiotelephone, echo sounder, radar, and Decca navigator.

SHRIMP BOATS

Shrimp boats land one of America's largest and most valuable catches. The bulk comes from the Gulf of Mexico, where new shrimp grounds have been discovered westward of the Florida Keys along the Gulf coast of the United States and Mexico as far south as Campeche Bank. Smaller quanti-

Fig. 45. Australian Prawn Catcher Boat. The worldwide growth of prawn and shrimp fisheries has brought the Gulf rig to South America, Alaska, the Persian Gulf and to Australia. *Lady of Fatima* fishes from the state of Western Australia. Sixty-two feet overall, she can steam at 10½ knots with a 5 ton catch on board. She drags two 60 foot prawning nets.

ties are taken off the South Atlantic states and in Alaskan waters. A large migratory fleet of trawlers follow seasonal movement of shrimp. Sailing from ports in Mexico, Central America, and the southern United States, they congregate wherever the catch proves best.

Most modern shrimpers are double-rigged; that is, they tow a large trawl from each of their two outriggers (fig. 44). A small try net is also towed over the stern. The outriggers or towing booms are swung outboard, then held in position by topping lifts, bow stays, and back stays. From the trawl winch a single warp runs along each outrigger to a towing block at its outboard end. Thence the warp runs down and aft to a bridle, each end of which is secured to a trawl door. The doors spread the wings of the trawl to its full width of 40 to 100 feet. Port and starboard warps are paid out with about 25 fathoms difference in length to separate the two nets.

After a drag, which may last about three hours in depths of 30 to 300 fathoms, the shorter warp is hauled in first. The "lazy line" is picked up and taken to a gypsy head to haul the trawl close alongside, clear of the propeller. The process is then repeated on the long side. Then the main fish tackle and the main boom, which is fixed on the center line, swing the cod ends on board with the catch.

Shrimpers are relatively small, usually under 100 feet, and driven by diesels up to 350 horsepower (fig. 130). The more powerful boats tow the larger trawls and work the distant grounds. Alaskan boats make daily trips and, in their cool climate, do not require refrigeration. Gulf and South Atlantic boats, making longer voyages, ice or freeze their catch.

Most foreign shrimpers are built along Gulf of Mexico lines. Figure 45 shows *Lady of Fatima*, an Australian prawn boat with a typical double rig. In the 1960's shrimping has boomed in the Persian Gulf, and there is a growing fleet based at Kuwait. Norway and the United States have fur-

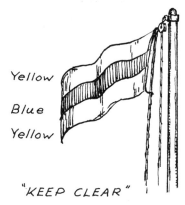

Fig. 46. International Code Flag "D". Pair trawlers fly this signal flag to warn other shipping to keep clear.

nished new boats of American type, but Poland's Centromor has built a 20-boat group of markedly different design. The deckhouse is aft and the mast and booms are forward. Gallows are fitted as well as outriggers.

An American shrimper, still in the prototype stage, has a catamaran hull. Besides high speed, twin hulls give a wide

40

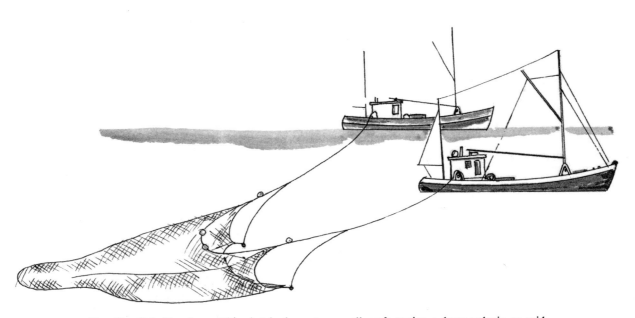

Fig. 47. Pair Trawlers. This sketch shows two small craft towing a large pelagic or mid-water trawl. The distance between the boats keeps the trawl wings open without the need of otter boards. The trawlers change speed to regulate the depth of their net, slowing to let it sink and speeding up to bring it closer to the surface. Trawl depth is selected to match the depth of schools located by fish-finder sonars.

uncluttered deck with ample working area. Hydraulically operated winches and booms simplify trawl handling. An innovation in working craft, a successful double hull could revolutionize fishing boat design.

Fig. 48. Chinese Fishing Junk. Guided by eyes painted on either bow, this two-masted junk fishes the East China sea off the mouth of the Yangtze. Each area has its own hull design and mast arrangement. The centuries-old four-sided lug sail, heavily battened, is common to all. Lacking engines, junks favor pair trawls with their lower power requirement. Most fishing junks have flush decks, moderate freeboard, and large windlasses.

PAIR TRAWLERS

Pair trawling is practiced either by small boats lacking sufficient power to drag a trawl alone or by bigger craft towing a very large net. Both bottom and pelagic (midwater) trawls are used, and they are found in all parts of the world. European drifters sometimes shift to pair trawling. In the Baltic, midwater trawlers steam in pairs at distances of 250 to 500 feet (fig. 47). The trawl is maintained at least 5 fathoms below the surface. At night, besides normal trawler running lights, they make special searchlight signals. After attracting attention, the two boats train their searchlight beams to cross between the vessels. Then the beams are swung back and forth, fore and aft, to show the location of the trawl between the vessels. Other craft should, of course, avoid passing between the pair of trawlers. Belgian pair trawlers make the same signals, and by day may also fly the International Code signal flag "D" (fig. 46) meaning "Keep clear of me; I am maneuvering with difficulty." Spanish pair trawlers, when approached by other vessels, burn a flare on the side where the trawl is rigged.

Pareja or paranzella fishing is a form of pair trawling originated by Italian and Spanish craft. Parejas are medium-sized vessels resembling either drifters or trawlers. They carry a large winch but lack gallows and otter boards. Their trawl, sometimes as wide as 300 feet, is double the size of a normal otter trawl. To spread the wings, the parejas steam 1000 yards apart. After a drag lasting several hours, one boat passes its warp to the other, which hauls the net on board over the bows.

Fig. 49. Oyster Dredge. This skipjack is running free on the port tack, towing a dredge on the starboard side amidships. The dredge consists of an iron frame spreading open a bag of rope and chain. The lower arm of the frame has rake-like teeth to loosen the oysters from the bottom. Chesapeake watermen design their own dredges, selecting size and shape to suit their individual preferences.

Pair trawling is common in the Oriental fishing fleets. Chinese sampans, both sail and power, fish in this way. The two-boat bull trawl is the mainstay of the Japanese eastern Pacific ground fishery. Working from mother ships, the bull trawlers measure about 100 feet overall and carry a crew of 12 men.

SAILING CRAFT

In some parts of the world sailboats are still used to tow trawls and dredges. The Brixham trawler (fig. 27b) is one of the few left in the English near-water fisheries. In America's Chesapeake Bay there remains a fleet of sailing dredgers. The conservation laws of Maryland, to preserve the oyster stock, prohibit dredging from power boats. As a result a fleet of several score of bugeyes and skipjacks work the oyster fishery, roaming the upper Bay with their dredges as they have since colonial days. Although they have no engines, each boat carries a small tender with inboard motor. When cruising in calms or light airs, the "yawl boat" pushes from astern. Sails alone must be used while dredging. Skipjacks are V-bottomed sloops; bugeyes round-bottomed ketches. Lengths range from 30 to 50 feet. Both types have clipper bows and broad beams with masts raked strongly aft. Shallow draft and centerboard allow them to sail in shoal water and to moor in the Chesapeake's shallow harbors (figs. 26, 49, and 131).

Although exact data are unavailable, mainland China is one of the world's leading fishing nations. In 1963 the Food and Agriculture Organization of the United Nations estimated the Chinese fisheries to be the third largest in the world, exceeded only by Japan and Peru. Much of their catch is taken by pair trawling junks. A typical fishing junk (fig. 48) has two or sometimes three masts and measures about 100 feet overall. Her silhouette is lower than the three- or four-masted cargo junk's, and she has heavier windlasses, mounted athwartships and turned by that most reliable prime mover—manpower. Like other junks the trawler has a broad beam, a centerboard, high bow, heavily battened sails, and painted eyes on the bows.

Junks, like fishing craft the world over, are being motorized. In Hong Kong, for example, engines have been installed in over half the fleet.

44

III. Hook-and-Line Craft

Trollers, longliners, tuna clippers and bottom fishermen comprise the chief types of hook-and-line boats. Trollers fish while underway, trailing lures or baited hooks astern. Longliners set baited hooks fastened to lines of two types: either buoyed to remain in the upper layers of the sea or weighted to lie on the bottom. The lines range in length from a hundred fathoms tended by an open boat to tens of miles shot and hauled by an oceangoing craft. Dorymen fish by longline, but rather than tending the lines directly they carry numbers of dories that run individual lines. Tuna clippers and the similar Japanese skipjack boats catch feeding tuna on hand-tended poles and lines. Bottom fishermen anchor or lie to and lower weighted hooks and lines to the bottom.

While trawlers and seiners with their specialized nets and handling gear have developed characteristic lines, hook-and-line craft differ widely in shape. Some of the large clippers and dorymen are long-range oceangoing vessels capable of cruises far from home. At the other extreme are open boats —skiffs, canoes, and dugouts—that fish inshore waters. Between are craft of every size and shape including some sailing boats. Fishermen in United States waters operate about five million hooks and baits.

Fig. 50. Salmon Troller. These small craft fish from the Alaskan panhandle south to California. Icing down the catch permits trips of up to two weeks. The troller's gurdy can handle a longline when the fisherman shifts from salmon to halibut.

TUNA CLIPPERS

The United States tuna fishery has developed in the twentieth century into one of the country's largest, both in weight and in value of catch. The fleet, formerly dominated by pole-and-line tuna clippers (fig. 51), now contains many purse seiners. The large Japanese tuna fleet includes clippers, seiners, and longliners. The clipper is also used in the Australian, New Zealand, and French tuna fisheries.

The method of fishing, together with the location of the tuna grounds, determines the clipper's design. Tuna are attracted alongside by throwing overboard quantities of live bait fish. These have been previously taken by lift or lampara nets and kept in tanks of circulating sea water. When feeding on the bait fish, the tuna strike readily on a baitless jig hook. Because of the large weight of the tuna, two or three poles and lines are fastened to a single hook with a fisherman manning each pole. Fishing from the fantail or a low platform aft, the fishermen swing the catch on deck, shake it off the hook, and repeat the process until the school stops feeding. Dozens of tuna weighing 25 pounds or more may be caught from one school. The catch is put in refrigerated brine wells until frozen. The brine is then pumped out and the fish stored dry at a temperature of 10° to 20° Fahrenheit.

The main fishing grounds for U.S. clippers are the warm waters off the west coast of the United States, Mexico, and Central and South America. Japanese clippers fish the same waters, as well as grounds in the southeast and northwest Atlantic. The remoteness of these areas requires long transits.

The clipper design resulting from these factors is a rugged craft up to 200 feet in length capable of carrying up to 500 tons of frozen fish. A high bow adds to seaworthiness. This together with the forward location of the superstructure gives a sheltered area for the fish deck and bait tank aft.

Fig. 51. Tuna Clipper. The largest American fishing craft, the clipper ranges farthest from home port and may spend two months at sea. This view shows the low stern with fishing platform surrounding the fish pound.

The boats for bait fishing and sometimes a seaplane or helicopter are also stowed aft. The high mast carries a crow's nest and the topping lift for the boat handling boom. Powerful diesels, large refrigeration plant, and quarters for

Fig. 52. Japanese Pole-and-Line Craft. *Chokyu Maru* was built in 1963 at Shimizu on the southern coast of Honshu. Japanese yards can complete a boat like this in two months. Japan's shipbuilding industry, skillful seamen, and taste for seafood make her one of the world's leading fishing nations.

a crew of twelve to fourteen result in a craft able to keep the sea for two or three months in distant waters.

Japanese pole-and-line craft are smaller than the clippers, averaging no more than 120 feet in length. They have a characteristic clipper bow with engines aft. Figure 52 shows

Fig. 53. Longlining. The crew sets the longline over the stern. Glass floats with bamboo pole markers, stowed on the fantail, are secured at the end of each 150 fathom "basket" of line.

Chokyu Maru II, grossing 240 tons. A 700 horsepower diesel drives her 117 foot steel hull at 12 knots. Craft of this type are active in the eastern Atlantic, landing their catches of albacore and skipjack in African ports.

TUNA LINE BOATS

Japanese longliners range the world over. With tuna as their chief quarry, they work in the North and South Pacific, the Atlantic, and the Indian Oceans. Much of their half million ton catch is exported, often by factory ships which process the catcher boats' tuna on the grounds and deliver it direct to European and American ports. The catch includes the four principal species of tuna, ranging in size from the twenty pound skipjack through albacore and yellowfin to the giant bluefins weighing up to half a ton.

A typical Japanese longliner (fig. 54) is an oceangoing craft up to 1300 tons gross and 200 feet overall. Similar in appearance to a coastal freighter with diesel and superstructure aft, she has a high forecastle with fish deck between forecastle and superstructure. The gear is arranged to handle up to 50 miles of line coiled on the after deck handy to the stowage for floats, markers and bait. The line is set over the stern and hauled forward. On the fish deck are either a power line-hauling winch or alternatively a crew of manual line haulers. The line is heaved on board over a roller at the deck edge, the catch is removed, and the line hauled aft along a chute leading to the poop deck. (fig. 53). The tuna are struck below for freezing and cold storage.

Other nations fish longlines also. The American exploratory fishing vessel *Delaware* has experimented with a power operated reel and "level-wind" spooling device. The reel holds 20 miles of quarter-inch main line. Every 20 fathoms

Fig. 54. Japanese Longliner. This medium-sized tuna boat grosses about 400 tons and carries a crew of 30 to 40 men. The conveyor, earmark of a longliner, carries gear from the forward fish deck aft to the stowage on the stern. To shoot and recover a 40 to 50 mile line requires a full day. The 2000 hooks may take two or three hundred tuna as well as sharks and billfish.

it is looped and knotted. The line is set by unreeling it through fairleads over the side. Branch lines or gangions, five fathoms long and baited with squid or herring, are clipped to each loop as it clears the fairleads. After every ten baits, a buoy on ten fathoms of buoy line is clipped to the longline to keep it at the proper depth. The aim of the installation is to reduce manpower, and the hauling crew has been successfully cut from six to four hands.

Fig. 55. Canadian Longliner. The fishing industry of Canada is growing rapidly as larger, more modern craft join the fleet. Longliners have replaced the dorymen who once fished the Atlantic Banks.

The Republic of Korea is entering the tuna fishery with a fleet of 75 new longliners built in Italy and France. Designed along Japanese lines, they are about 100 feet in length grossing 140 tons. These are to be the nucleus of a 600-vessel fishing fleet including craft built in Japan and Korea as well as in Europe.

LONGLINERS

Tuna are taken on longlines set near the surface—"pelagic longlines." In other fisheries the lines and hooks lie on the bottom. This is the rig used for taking halibut in the waters off the Pacific coast of North America. In 1923 the United States and Canada formed the International Pacific Halibut Commission; this body manages the halibut stocks, setting seasons and catch limits in prescribed ocean areas. The halibut fishery supports a 400-boat American and Canadian fleet, with the Canadian boats generally larger, newer, and faster. Japan has recently entered the fishery under the terms of the U.S.-Canada-Japan North Pacific Fisheries Commission.

The halibut schooner (fig. 56) is a relatively small craft, often a combination vessel also adaptable to seining or trawling. Like other longliners she has a deck edge roller and line hauler for bringing the line on board, and carries floats and markers to buoy the ends of the line. A peculiarity of fishermen in these waters is the stabilizer. Designed to reduce rolling at slow speeds, the stabilizer is a board several square feet in area weighted to ride horizontally. A stabilizer is hung from an outrigger on each side of the boat, with the line adjusted to keep the board 10 to 20 feet under water. Rolling to one side drags the opposite stabilizer upward; water resistance reduces the amount of roll. Steadying sails are also set to increase stability.

Other longline fisheries lie in the North Sea and northeast Atlantic. British "great liners" sail out of Aberdeen.

Fig. 56. Halibut Longliner. The halibut schooner fishes from Alaska to Oregon. A typical craft is 80 feet overall, built of wood, and diesel propelled. A crew of six make two to three week trips. The Pacific fisherman calls the longline a "setline"; the New Englander, a "trawl line"; in southern waters it is a "trotline."

Norway operates large modern craft of about 130 feet overall with 1000 horsepower engines and 12 knot speed. Equipped with freezers and refrigerated holds, these combination boats are fitted as seiner/longliners or as stern trawler/longliners. In a new approach American, Canadian, and Japanese longliners are taking record catches of swordfish off the east coast of North America. Their lines are

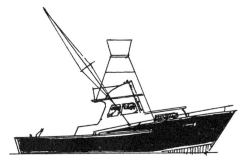

Fig. 57. Sport Fisherman. Tuna, marlin, tarpon, and sailfish are among the favorites of the big game fishermen. The skipper conns the boat from the flying bridge where he can watch for strikes on the trolled baits. The fisherman plays the fish from a special chair at the stern.

similar to tuna gear, with hooks buoyed near the surface. Figure 55 shows the new Canadian boat *Dorothy and Gail*. Japanese demersal longliners, working from mother ships, take cod, sablefish, and rockfish in the Bering Sea ground fisheries. The dory fisheries of the Grand Banks are described in a later section.

TROLLERS

Trolling is fishing by towing a lure or baited hook astern of a slowly moving boat. A common method of sport fishing, it is also used commercially to take salmon off the west coast of North America and tuna in western European waters.

Figures 50 and 58 show typical salmon trollers from the Pacific States, British Columbia, or southern Alaska. Normally 60 feet or less overall, they are handy enough for a crew of one or two. Their gear is trolled from four outriggers, a long pair aft and a shorter pair forward. These can be secured in the vertical position or guyed outboard for fishing. From the end of each outrigger, a tag line and chain suspend a clothespin line snap at the water's edge. For each outrigger a wire trolling line runs from a separate gurdy spool to a davit and thence to the tag line clothespin. From the clothespin the line leads down to a cannonball sinker weighing up to 50 pounds. Six or eight baited hooks or lures are snapped to each trolling line by connectors attached to 2 to 3 fathom leaders. The gear is arranged so that the helmsman can conn the boat, run the gurdy, and handle the catch by himself.

The fisherman trolls at one or two knots, streaming stabilizers to steady the boat. When a jerk at the end of an outrigger shows that a fish is hooked, the helmsman hauls in the line by energizing the appropriate gurdy spool. He unsnaps the trolling line from the tag line when the clothespin reaches the deck edge, and unsnaps empty leaders as

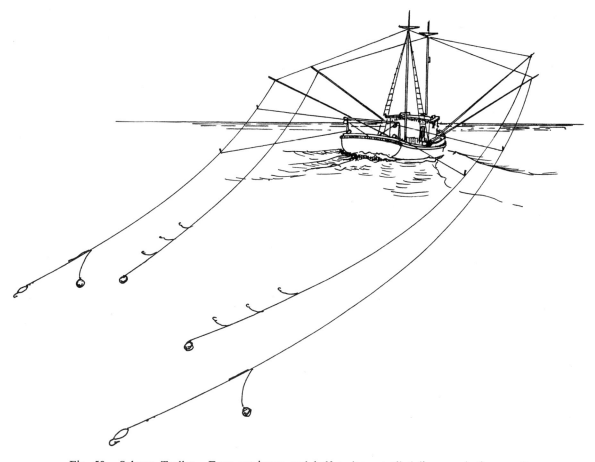

Fig. 58. Salmon Troller. Four outriggers and half a dozen trolled lines mark these craft of the Pacific northwest. Each line carries several lures or baits as well as a heavy cannonball sinker. A power operated gurdy helps retrieve the heavy gear and catch.

53

they are brought alongside. When he reaches the leader with the hooked fish, the fisherman hauls it in by hand until he can gaff the catch and swing it on board. As soon as possible the salmon are dressed, struck below and iced for the ten-day to two-week cruise.

A typical sport fisherman is shown in figure 57. These boats operate off both coasts of the Americas. Several lines are trolled from rods and reels, some directly over the stern and some via outriggers. Many species of game fish are taken, with swordfish, marlin, and tuna among the most popular.

SHARK SCHOONERS

Sharks are taken in all the oceans, both for direct consumption and as a source of vitamins from the liver oil. The mako, thresher, and tiger are also taken by sportsmen as big game fish. Large sharks reach twenty feet or more in length. Too heavy for netting, they are caught on baited hooks, either singly or on longlines (fig. 60). Japan and Norway take large catches, with smaller fisheries in the United States and the Western European countries. The annual catch in tropical waters is small but important. Salted and then sun dried, shark meat is a significant part of the total tropical catch and furnishes an essential source of protein in the diet.

The Indian Ocean supports a small but centuries-old shark fishery. In recent years exploratory fishing and improved methods have brought in new areas. One of these

is the Seychelles, an island group a thousand miles east of Mombasa and 250 miles south of the Equator. From the abyssal sea bed 2000 fathoms down a shallow submarine plateau rises to a depth of 40 fathoms. Scattered over the plateau are a dozen small islands. The islands support a fleet of shark "schooners"—small auxiliaries or sailing craft

Fig. 59. *Golden Bells*. A Seychelle Islands "schooner," *Golden Bells* is typical of Indian Ocean shark longliners. Her two headsails, short mast, and gaff-rigged mainsail are better adapted to a working sailboat than the high masts and Bermuda rig of modern racing yachts.

of various rigs. *Golden Bells* (fig. 59) is typical, a 38 foot cutter grossing six tons. With a crew of half a dozen, boats like this fish the *bordage*—the edge of the plateau. Here schools of bait fish attract large sharks.

Lacking refrigeration, the Seychelles fishermen catch their bait by handline on the grounds. Larger gear is used for the

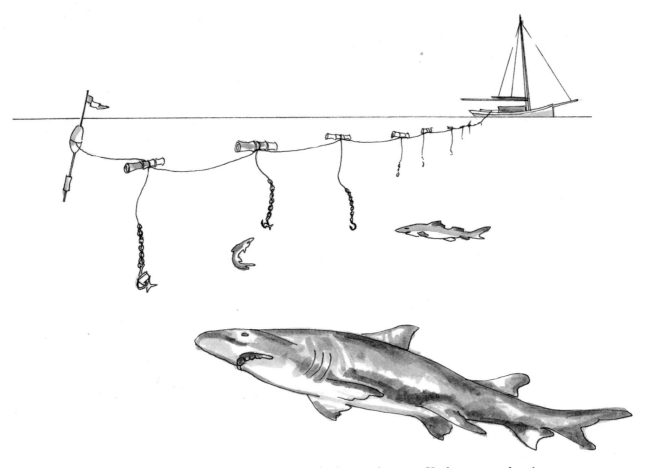

Fig. 60. Shark Longline. Shark gear must be large and strong. Hooks, up to a foot long, are secured to lengths of chain. It takes several men to land a twenty foot mako. In primitive fisheries the catch is salted, then dried in the sun. Modern boats fillet and freeze the meat and dry the fins, an Oriental delicacy.

55

sharks: twenty-five fathom tarred lines each carrying a six inch hook on a three foot chain. The bitter end is secured to a ring bolt on deck and the baited hook dropped overboard. Three or four men fish at a time, each tending a line. When a shark is hooked the other lines are hauled in. Several men hand-play the shark until it can be brought to the surface. One man then nooses its head with a heavy wire to relieve the strain on the lighter shark line. Another kills the shark with blows of a wooden maul and jabs of a

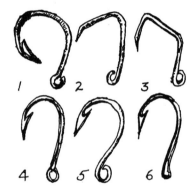

Fig. 61. Hooks.
1. Circle   4. Salmon
2,3. Squid   5,6. Cod

harpoon. The carcass is manhandled on board, gutted, cut into slabs, and salted down in the hold. After a ten-day trip the schooner returns to port where the meat is sun-dried for export.

56

GLOUCESTER FISHERMEN

For almost a century, from 1850 to 1940, the Gloucester fishing schooner was Queen of the Banks. In 1847 a Massachusetts shipbuilder launched *Romp*, a fisherman with the lines of a pilot schooner. Sailing out of Gloucester, she was so successful that her design was copied throughout New England and the Maritime Provinces. The term Gloucesterman came to be applied to schooners of the entire area. Soon similar craft were fishing from George's Bank, off Cape Cod, to the Grand Banks of Newfoundland. Their salt cod sold from Boston to St. John, New Brunswick.

By 1857 the schooners had taken on a clipper design: longer, sharper, and faster, with a large sail plan. In 1884 the design changed again as the clipper bow and jibboom gave way to a plumb stem and spike bowsprit. Lengths passed 100 feet, sail areas increased still more, and speeds grew higher. Schooners logged 15.4 knots on the run from George's Bank to Boston Light, 15.6 from Cape Sable to Gloucester.

The drive for higher speed continued, both for economic reasons—first to market meant highest prices—and from the skippers' pure competitive spirit. Fishermen turned to yacht designers for faster hulls. By 1900 *Helen M. Gould* measured 125 feet overall, and the last working "Gloucester" schooner, the Nova Scotian *Bluenose*, measured 143 feet. The schooners were as rugged as they were fast; straight grained yellow pine trenailed to close-spaced oak frames

Fig. 62.   Gloucester Schooner.   Launched in Essex, Massachusetts, in 1921, *L. A. Dunton* fished the Banks until 1935. Her masts were shortened, a diesel installed, dories removed, and she gave up fishing for cargo carrying in the coastal trade. In 1963 the Marine Historical Association bought her. Original rig restored, she is berthed at the Mystic Seaport in Connecticut—the last of the dorymen.

fitted them for service in their treacherous home waters. *Bluenose*, for example, sailed for 25 years until she struck a reef and was lost.

The schooners carried a dozen or more two-man dories nested on deck. On the grounds the dories fished longlines. In good weather or bad, foggy or clear, the dories pulled away in the morning and back in the evening . . . if they could find the schooner. Bad weather sank many a dory and a number of schooners.

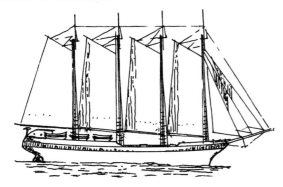

Fig. 63. Portuguese Lugger. American and Canadian schooners have left the Banks, but Portugal still takes cod with sailing craft, open dories, and longlines. After a ceremony in Lisbon and the blessing of the fleet, the luggers sail each spring for the western Atlantic grounds. Half a year later they set their sails to the prevailing westerlies and return to Portugal with holds full of salted cod.

After the first World War auxiliaries and then power boats, safer and more reliable, began to replace the schooner. Sails shrank and gradually vanished as the dragger and the longliner took the place of the Gloucesterman. In 1940 a handful remained, and today there are only two. *Bluenose II*, a replica of her namesake, sails for pleasure and for publicity; *L. A. Dunton*, built in 1921, has been preserved at Mystic Seaport, Connecticut (fig. 62). Only the Portuguese luggers still work the Banks in the traditional way.

DORYMEN

Four centuries old, the Newfoundland cod fishery is still worked by Portuguese dorymen. Parts of the Grand Banks, too rocky to trawl without damage to nets and gear, can only be fished by longlines. Each April a fleet of about 70 Portuguese dorymen sails from the Tagus for a cruise lasting six to eight months. Except for occasional visits to St. John for bait and rest, they stay at sea until the catch is complete.

About half of the fleet are motor vessels. The rest are luggers, four-masted schooners with powerful diesel auxiliaries. A typical lugger (fig. 63) is trim and modern in design, about 150 feet overall, grossing between 600 and 1000 tons. Her auxiliary engine delivers 400 to 600 horsepower. She carries gaff rigged sails on four masts, spreading about 5500 square feet of canvas. The schooner rig is easy to handle, and sail power increases endurance while reducing fuel cost. Nested on deck are 50 to 100 one-man dories (fig. 114). A crew of 50 to 60 men work the ship, man the dories, and handle the catch. The luggers carry modern navigational gear including radar and radio direction finders.

Fig. 64. Motor Doryman. Like the luggers, Portuguese dorymen fish the Banks from spring
to fall. A mother ship (fig. 104) accompanies the fleet to provide medical attention, stores,
repairs, and to transport home a part of the catch. *Senhora da Boa Viagem,* pictured here,
has a white hull with buff superstructure and stack. Each dory carries on its bows the firm's
stack insignia—white cross on blue background with the letter *A* in the center.

The motor doryman (fig. 64) is somewhat similar in appearance to the lugger. Two unusually high masts carry antennas, the topping lift for the cargo boom, and a triatic stay. The stay supports falls for the dories. A catwalk from the after superstructure to the forecastle allows safe passage fore and aft when the waist is taking green water. Dories

Fig. 65. Snapper Schooner. Snapper boats fish the shallow coastal waters of the Gulf of Mexico from the Florida Keys to Campeche Bank. Diesel has replaced canvas for propulsion in the newer craft, but their tall masts and clean lines reflect the tradition of sail. Hand-lines were formerly coiled in kegs; today they are wound on reels driven by bicycle chains and two-handed cranks.

are stacked fore and aft. On the bow of each neatly painted boat is her number and a replica of the firm's stack insignia.

Life is safer and more comfortable for the lugger crewman than it was a century ago. Radar can locate the dories, and an engine helps recover them if the wind is too light or too strong for the sails. Auxiliary power gives heat, light, and other amenities missing from the forecastle of a wooden

schooner. But the sea is as dangerous and unpredictable as ever, and it still takes a brave and skillful seaman to fish the high seas alone in a dory.

SAILING CRAFT

Since hook-and-line fishing places few demands on vessel design, a variety of sailing craft have been used in these fisheries. Sail survives not only on the Grand Banks, but also in the Caribbean and Gulf of Mexico snapper fishery. In these warm waters large schooners fish banks well off-shore. Based in the Gulf states, in Cuba, and in Venezuela, some are veterans of the Newfoundland Banks while others are new motor sailers with diesel auxiliaries. A typical older schooner is 100 feet in length, gaff rigged on two masts with a huge mainsail whose boom reaches aft of the counter. Even stripped of her topmasts, she shows the yacht-like lines of the Gloucester doryman. A modern snapper schooner is the cypress, mahogany, and pine *Lou Belle* (fig. 65). Built in Alabama and based in Florida, this 74 foot two-master has a 230 horsepower diesel capable of driving her at 10 knots. On the banks, a snapper boat fishes a dozen or more hand lines each carrying 15 to 20 baited hooks and a heavy sinker. A lucky boat may catch a ton of snapper and grouper in a day. Fish are either iced or kept alive in a "live well."

Another colorful sailer was the Breton tuna boat or *thonier* (fig. 66). Seaworthy yawls and ketches, they were 60 to 70 feet long with a wide beam and deep draft. Gaff

Fig. 66. Thonier. Breton fishermen used to take tuna or *thon* from gaff-rigged yawls and ketches. Bluff bow and wide counter stern, heavy pole mainmast and long bowsprit gave the tunnyman a distinctive appearance. Sails and hull were brightly colored—a tradition carried on by their motor powered successors today. The last of Europe's sailing fishermen, the soundly built *thonier* fleets sailed until the late 1940's.

61

rigged main and mizzen plus topsail, jib, and forestaysail drove the *thonier* at a five knot trolling speed. Horsehair lures were streamed from port and starboard outriggers or *tangons*, half a dozen to each outrigger, from the counter, and from the mizzen masthead. Based at Concarneau, Douarnenez, and other South Britanny ports, a fleet of 600 to 750 tunnymen followed the schools that annually migrated north across the Bay of Biscay. Lacking ice or refrigeration, the boats would take several hundred fish in a ten day cruise and return to port at top speed racing against spoilage.

Today most *thoniers* are diesel auxiliaries. They carry a modest spread of canvas divided among jib, main and mizzen, usually jib-headed but sometimes with a gaff. The *tangons*, twice as tall as the mast, are guyed from the main. Brightly painted blue or green hulls and tan sails combine with the outriggers to give them a distinctive appearance. Breton tunnymen take their 75-footers far from home port, sometimes as far as 500 miles in the rough North Atlantic.

IV. Gill Netters

Gill netters are classified either as drifters or bottom netters. Drifters fish nets buoyed to hang at the surface. They shoot their nets as they steam slowly downwind, then tie up to the leeward end and drift until it is time to haul the nets. Bottom set nets, as the name implies, are weighted so that their lower edge lies on the ocean floor. They are fitted with a corkline along the upper edge of the net, but its buoyancy is insufficient to keep the entire rig afloat. Bottom netters do not ride to their nets. They cast off and buoy the ends, usually with a lighted or a radio buoy to facilitate finding it again.

Net boats usually have a low, clear deck edge over which to haul and shoot the nets. They lack the heavy booms and winches of the purse seiner or trawler. Manpower formerly handled the nets and has proven difficult to replace. Gill netting has not lent itself to automation, with the result that the stern trawler and the purse seiner have replaced the drifter in some fisheries. This transition has been especially important in the North Sea, an historic drift net fishery. In the United States the majority of the drift nets are operated on the Pacific salmon grounds.

DRIFTERS OF NORTHERN EUROPE

The North Sea has long supported drifter fleets from all the countries washed by its tides. Scottish and English east

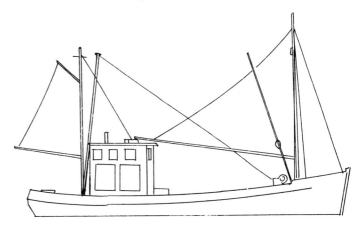

Fig. 67. Scottish Herring Drifter. A diesel-driven double-ender, the herring drifter is of wooden construction, usually clinker built. The steadying sail keeps her headed into the seas while drifting to her nets.

coast fishermen set their gill nets on its banks beside Norwegians, Danes, Germans, Belgians, Dutch, and French. The Baltic fleets include drifters from Sweden, Germany, and Poland. Appearance and nomenclature of the boats vary from country to country. Large West German boats, for example, are called *motorloggers* or *luggers* (fig. 68).

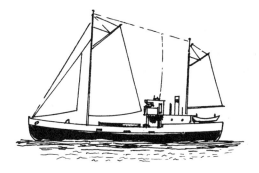

Fig. 68. West German Motor Lugger. These vessels fish herring gill nets in the North Sea. The more efficient purse seiners and midwater trawlers are replacing the drifters in this important fishery.

Smaller types are termed *kutters*, a name also applied to Danish and Dutch craft. Most drifters are flush decked with engines aft. Their high foremast is usually mounted in a tabernacle. Modern boats are diesel engined. Figure 69 shows an older type English drifter. A high thin stack shows that she is steam powered. Like other small fishermen she carries a steadying sail on the mizzen to reduce rolling and to keep her headed into the wind.

Drifters display various marks and lights to warn other shipping of the location of their nets. Danish cutters mark one end of the fleet of nets by night with a white light, by day with a black barrel or a buoy with a triangular flag. Swedish fishermen show a white light at one of the nets, a violet light at the other. The British use a white float or a staff with a flag. International Rules of the Road require drifters to burn a red light over a white light on the mast, together with a lower white light offset in the direction of the nets. By day the red and white lights are replaced by a pair of cones, the offset white light by a single cone, point upward. Small craft hang a basket in the rigging. Other craft should pass to leeward, on the opposite side from the single cone, offset white light, or basket.

In recent years drifters have been giving way to pelagic (midwater) trawlers and to purse seiners. An apparent change in the habits of the herring, plus the introduction of fish-finding sonar which allows fishermen to locate and track the schools, has made the "hunting" methods (seining and trawling) more productive than the "trapping" methods (gill netting). A labor shortage at sea has also put the drifter at a disadvantage, since gill nets require more hands than trawl gear. Working against the trawl, conversely, is the large engine power required; against the purse seiner is the difficulty of handling the seine without fouling the screw. As a result many new boats are built from the keel up as combination craft, able to select the type of gear best suited to conditions at a particular place and season.

Fig. 69. English Steam Drifter. An obsolete and vanishing type, the steam drifter has been outmoded by diesel propulsion. Their well built hulls give them a long life, however; some drifters are still fishing after 50 years at sea. This boat has lowered her foremast and set a gaff-rigged steadying sail to decrease rolling.

SCOTTISH HERRING BOATS

A traditional Scottish fishery is gill netting for herring in the North and Norwegian Seas. Reaching the grounds at dusk, the "drifter" moves slowly downwind, shooting its nets as it goes (fig. 70). After its mile-long "fleet" of nets has been paid out, the boat secures the lead line forward, rigs its steadying sail aft, and drifts to the nets. At dawn

Fig. 70. Shooting a Gill Net. These fishermen are shooting or setting a net from a Scottish drifter. The roller reduces friction and eases handling the heavy gear. A crew of six mans the 75 foot craft on her nightly trips.

the nets are hauled, the fish removed, and the drifter returns to port. Short trips are the rule, since few drifters have refrigeration and the catch must be landed promptly.

Scottish drifters work from ports on both coasts and in the Northern Isles, with a fleet of some 50 boats in the Shetlands. Typically they are small double-enders, diesel powered, with wheelhouse aft (figs. 67 and 71). There is a roller, sometimes power driven, on the starboard rail, and a capstan forward. The mast is often mounted in a tabernacle which permits it to be lowered to increase stability. Small trawlers have similar hulls and houses, but mount a winch rather than a capstan, are fitted with gallows, and do not lower their masts.

Herring normally inhabit the bottom and midwaters by day, the upper waters at night. Skippers with fish-finder echo sounders try to locate schools during the day and lay their nets in those areas, planning to catch the fish as they rise at dark. Others, without modern equipment, select their ground from past experience or from observation of other boats. As a result drifters tend to congregate, and their nets cover large areas of the sea. The U.S. Navy's Hydrographic Office advises:

"Vessels should, if possible, avoid passing through a fleet of drifters. Even a single vessel may have difficulty in doing so without damage to the nets, as the nets of one boat lie so close to those of another that in maneuvering to pass the end of one line of drift nets a vessel is apt to find herself in the middle of another. If forced by circumstances to cross a line of drift nets, the least damage will be done

Fig. 71. Drifters at Great Yarmouth. Scottish boats join the local fleet offloading at this English East Coast fishing port at the mouth of the River Yare. Dwindling catches have reduced the fleet from its peak of over 1000 in 1913 to less than 100. Great Yarmouth boats have hull numbers preceded by the letters YH.

67

by crossing them at right angles, midway between two of their buoys, at a fair rate of speed. If possible propellers should be stopped while passing over the nets. The mere parting of a net does no great harm, but the revolving propeller may draw up the headlines and the net, thereby doing considerable damage. Cases have been reported of large steamers having to be towed into port, helpless after

Fig. 72. Alaskan Gill Netter. This 32 foot, 15 knot boat has an aluminum hull which reduces maintenance and increases fish capacity. The hydraulically driven drum holds the net; powered rollers immediately aft of the drum facilitate hauling and setting.

fouling drift nets . . . The best policy is to give drifters a wide berth at all times."

SALMON NETTERS

One of the largest and most valuable fisheries in North America is the salmon industry of Alaska, British Columbia, Washington, and Oregon. Salmon are taken by trolling, by purse seining, by traps, and by gill nets. Gill nets are worked by relatively small craft, averaging 25 to 40 feet in

length. With a crew of one or two, they normally fish in waters close to the cannery or cold storage plant. Most boats lack refrigeration and must catch and market the fish daily to avoid spoilage. Nets are usually set across river mouths. Where the water is clear, nets are set at dusk and hauled at dawn. Where silt reduces underwater visibility and the fish cannot see the webbing, nets are fished during the day. Nets are made of either natural fiber or nylon, and experimentally of monofilament. A typical net is several hundred fathoms in length, three fathoms deep, with mesh ranging from 5 to 10 inches. It must be cleaned and dried weekly.

Older gill netters are of wooden construction, slow and heavy. Some boats, termed "bow pickers," are fitted with a power roller and net stowage forward. More numerous are boats which work their nets aft. Figure 73 shows a typical Canadian craft. These have a roller across the transom, and in the after cockpit a powered net reel, four to six feet in diameter and several feet in length. The reel is driven by a chain or vee belt or, in the newest boats, hydraulically. To set the net, the bitter end is buoyed and dropped astern. The boat steams across the current, unreeling the net over the stern roller as it goes. After several hours, the net is reeled in at speeds up to 30 rpm, stopping when necessary to gaff the salmon and bring them on board.

Figure 72 shows a new aluminum net boat for the fishery of Cook Inlet, Alaska. Thirty-two feet in length, it is driven at 15 knots by a 165 horsepower gasoline engine. Aluminum

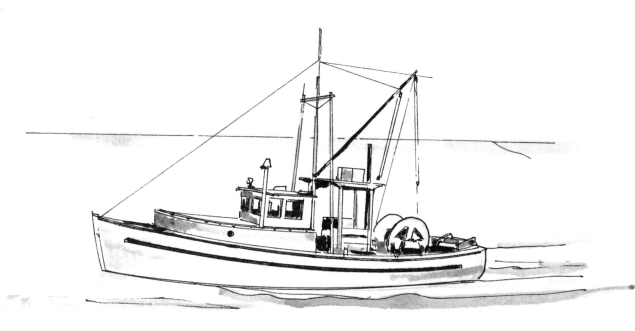

Fig. 73. Canadian Salmon Netter. Older than the aluminum craft in figure 72, this wooden gill netter fishes off the river mouths of British Columbia. Lacking refrigeration, it makes short trips and offloads daily. A typical boat is 28 feet long, draws 2 to 3 feet, and carries a one- or two-man crew.

provides a lightweight durable hull with accommodations for a crew of two and a 12 ton fish hold.

CATCHER BOATS

The fisheries of the North Pacific are worked to a large extent by mother ships and catcher boats from Japan and Russia. The salmon fleet uses pelagic gill nets. Bottom gill nets have been used experimentally to take groundfish in waters whose depth is too great or bottom topography un-

Fig. 74. Japanese *Kawasaki* Boat. The *Kawasaki* is a large motor skiff operating as a catcher boat from a mother craft. They set gill nets in the salmon and demersal fisheries of the North Pacific.

suited for trawling, the most common method of demersal fishing in that area. King crabs are taken in tangle nets set on the bottom.

Catcher boats are of two types: motor skiffs or *kawasakis* carried on the mother ship, and larger seagoing craft capable of steaming from home port to the grounds. Skiffs are about 30 feet long and of 8 to 10 gross tons (fig. 74); a typical factory ship carries up to a dozen. Japanese catcher boats

gross 80 to 100 tons, measure somewhat under 100 feet long, and steam at 8 or 9 knots (fig. 75). The crew numbers about 15. Nets are set from the stern and taken aboard by a power net hauler on the deck edge forward. The Russian catcher boat is a medium trawler (SRT) fitted out for gill netting. Larger than their Japanese counterparts, they range in size from 260 gross tons, 130 feet long, up to the *Okean* class of 505 tons, 167 feet. Besides power net haulers, they are equipped with shaking devices to speed removal of the catch. Catcher boats normally carry radar, radio direction finder, and echo sounders. Depending on the size of the mother ship, she may handle from 6 to 20 catchers.

Bottom set nets can be laid in depths up to 500 fathoms, well beyond the usual trawling depth. A set may be as long as a mile, and is often marked by a radio buoy to aid in relocating it. Glass floats are used even at these great depths, where the water pressure is over 1000 pounds per square inch. After hauling its net, a process requiring several hours, the catcher boat delivers its fish or crabs to the mother ship. In calm weather the ships tie up to each other for the transfer. In rough seas the catch is secured in a buoyed cargo net, thrown overboard, and towed across to the mother ship by a cable.

CARIBBEAN TURTLE SCHOONERS

For generations Cayman Island schooners have taken turtles along Nicaragua's Miskito Coast. Gaff-rigged two masters, the schooners sail each spring from the Caymans

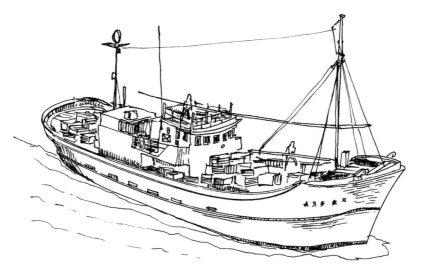

Fig. 75. Japanese Tangle Netter. This king crab boat is one of the 250 operating from Nemuro, a port at the eastern end of Hokkaido. After a good trip a catcher boat may land a five ton catch. Weighing several pounds each, with legs measuring two feet long, the crabs are taken in tangle nets set on the bottom.

to their advance base in the Miskito Islands (fig. 77). The crews have learned that turtles spend their days feeding on eelgrass in shallow coastal waters. At dusk they move seaward to spend the night among coral heads in depths up to 10 fathoms. The schooners cruise the deep waters by day to select the grounds for setting the evening's nets. Clear water allows the captain and the mates, high in the

Fig. 76. Loggerhead Turtle. These marine reptiles reach a weight of 200 pounds in eight to ten years. Record loggerheads weigh 800 pounds.

rigging, to search the bottom. The captain conns the ship while the mates look for likely coral heads. On orders from aloft, the crew mark them by dropping anchored buoys. After setting up to 100 markers, the schooner clears the

area and anchors. In the evening the crew sail back in their dugouts, clinker built 20-footers carrying three men and thirty 10-fathom tangle nets. Two men furl the sail, then row to the nearest marker. The third man secures the buoy to one end of the corkline and shoots the net over the stern as the oarsmen pull away. The far end is buoyed and anchored, and the process repeated. All nets laid, the dugout sails back to the schooner.

Returning at dawn, the crew hauls the nets, dragging the turtles aboard by their front flippers. Six or eight greens or loggerheads, weighing up to 300 pounds, make a heavy load for an open boat in a choppy sea. Back at the schooner the turtles are swung on board and stowed below. Turned upside down to prevent their heavy weight from collapsing their lungs, they breathe freely and can be kept alive for days. After a week's turtling the schooner returns to the advance base and off-loads the catch. The turtles are confined in a *kraal*, a bamboo walled enclosure in one of the island's shallow lagoons. With turtle hold empty and water casks refilled, the schooner returns to the grounds for another week. After several trips have filled the kraal, the schooner loads for the voyage to market. The turtles are recaptured, wrestled by hand into dugouts and back aboard the schooner. Hold and decks full of upside-down turtles, she sets a course for Jamaica, Panama, or southern Florida. The catch sold, the schooner returns to the Miskitos for more turtling until the autumn hurricanes close the season.

Fig. 77. Cayman Turtle Schooner. The Cayman Islands, 150 miles south of Cuba, are home port of the turtle fleet. The grounds lie 350 miles farther south in Nicaragua's Miskito Islands; the markets spread from Florida to Panama. Some schooners were built in the Caribbean; others are relics of the Grand Banks fisheries.

V. Purse Seiners

The large purse seine has revolutionized the North Sea herring fishery and the Pacific tuna fisheries. Modern gear, including power blocks, net haulers, side thrusters, and active rudders, have made it possible to utilize seines a mile in circumference and a thousand feet deep—much too big for manhandling. Blocks and net haulers pull the heavy seine on board; side thrusters and active rudders help the skipper maneuver his ship to avoid damaging the net during recovery. Suction pumps for taking the fish out of the bunt are replacing brail nets with a further reduction in manpower.

In the North Sea the purse seiner is replacing the drifter. Norwegian fishermen are ordering seiners at a rate which taxes the capacity of their shipyards. The vessels are growing in size, with a 180-footer scheduled for delivery in 1968. Whale catchers from the dying Norwegian whaling fleet have been converted to seiners. Steel construction is replacing wood except in the smaller sizes under about 70 feet. Great Britain, traditionally partial to the trawler and the drifter, is beginning to use the purse seine, and interest is growing in Iceland and the Scandinavian countries.

In America the purse seiner is replacing the clipper in the Pacific tuna fleet. Some are conversions from pole-and-line; others were built from the keel up as seiners. Similar boats fish for salmon in waters north of the tuna grounds. The Japanese fleet contains new purse seiners, some built along American Pacific lines, others resembling the Scandinavian craft.

Fig. 78. Hauling the Seine. These Japanese purse seiners are hauling their net. Large seines require as many as 70 men in five boats.

In other fisheries the purse seiner has been the traditional type. The Atlantic mackerel seiners and menhaden seiners have a long history, and the California herring and sardine boats have used the seine for decades.

MENHADEN SEINERS

Purse seiners take almost half of the annual United States catch. In the Gulf and the Atlantic this is chiefly menhaden —over 600,000 tons in a good year. The menhaden fleet includes nearly 250 craft, 40 in Chesapeake Bay alone. The boats have a distinctive silhouette: low hull with short forward deckhouse separated by a long fish hold from the

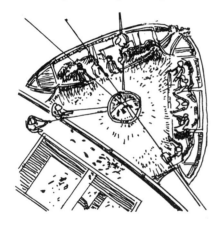

Fig. 79. Brailing Menhaden. Older seiners transfer the catch from the bunt of the net to the hold by brail. In modern rigs a suction hose and pump bring the catch on board.

engine room aft (fig. 80). A high mast supports the boom and crow's nest. In davits on port and starboard quarter is a 35 foot aluminum seine boat. Beamy double-enders, each mounts a power block on a large davit. Screened rudder

and propeller prevent fouling the net. The seine is stowed in the boats, half in each, ready to set.

Guided by lookouts aloft or in a light plane, the seiner approaches a school of menhaden and the crew mans the boats on the double. The captain lowers the seine boats and pulls clear. Lashed together, the boats steer to the edge of the school, then separate. Each takes a semicircular course, paying out the seine as they go. On the opposite side of the fish they join ends of the seine and haul in the purse line to close the bottom. Power blocks pull the wings into the boats and confine the fish in the bunt. The seiner comes alongside and takes the catch on board. Older boats scoop up the menhaden in brails (fig. 79). Newer seiners use suction pumps for greater speed and economy of manpower. Lacking refrigeration, seiners off-load nightly at their processing plant and resume operations early the next morning.

Few of the oily, smelly menhaden are eaten. Most are processed into meal and oil at shore plants. Fish meal is an ingredient of animal and chicken feed. Even though United States production exceeds 150,000 tons annually, the supply is insufficient and an equal amount is imported. Fish oil goes into such diverse products as paint, printing ink, and lipstick. Most is exported, chiefly to Europe. Of potential importance to the menhaden fishery is the development of "FPC" or fish protein concentrate. Entire fish— head, fins, tail, viscera and all—can be reduced to an edible powder containing most of the protein and minerals of the raw fish. Economical to produce, transport, and store,

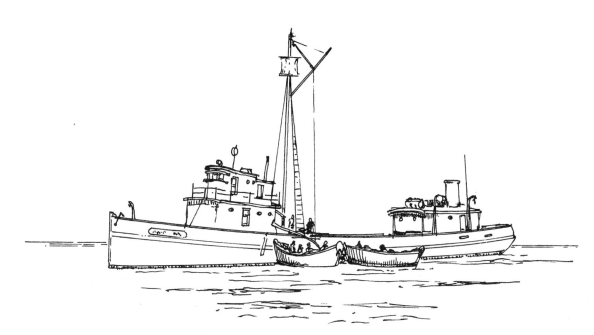

Fig. 80. Atlantic Purse Seiner. This menhaden boat is lying to alongside its net. The seine boats have hauled in the purse line and most of the net. The fish are held in the bunt, ready for loading. After the net is empty, the boats will be swung on the quarter davits with half the webbing in each.

FPC can have an immense impact by supplying the protein needs of the world's undernourished peoples.

SALMON BOATS

On the Pacific coast of the United States and Canada purse seiners take large catches of salmon. Modern equip-

Fig. 81. Drum Seiner. This Oregon purse seiner stows its net on the stern reel. The skiff assists in setting the net and in keeping the seiner from fouling its screw during recovery. The catch is usually herring or salmon.

ment allows these craft to handle the seine with only a few men and a single seine skiff. The drum seiner (fig. 81) mounts a 6 to 8 foot diameter reel or drum on his stern, either on deck or recessed in a well to keep the weight low. As wide as the beam will permit, the drum holds 250 to 300 fathoms of seine net. The main engine drives the reel either mechanically or hydraulically. A level wind spooling

device, a drum speed control, and a transom roller complete the rig.

To set the net, the bunt end, purse line, and corkline are secured to the skiff towed astern. When fish are found the skiff casts off and the seine is unreeled. The seiner steers in a straight line, keeping the seine and skiff dead astern. When the seine is fully paid out, the skiff starts his motor and overtakes the seiner on a slightly divergent course at a higher speed. This maneuver gives the seine a U-shape as it is towed slowly through the water. Finally the skiff comes alongside, closing the seine and passing cork and purse lines to the seiner. Then the skiff shifts to the opposite side, picks up a tow line, and pulls on it to keep the seiner from fouling the net. The seiner takes the purse line to his winch and hauls it in to close the bottom, simultaneously reeling the seine on the drum. The catch is either brailed out of the bunt or hauled on board over the stern roller.

In Alaskan and Canadian waters many salmon seiners are fitted with a power block and a rotating seine platform. Figure 82 shows *Gypsy Queen*. This type of boat has a forward deckhouse and a high, strongly stayed mast to support the seine boom. The after deck is clear, providing space to handle the catch and to stow seine and skiff. Cool climate and short runs to the cannery make refrigeration unnecessary.

TUNA PURSE SEINERS

The California seiner has set the style for tuna boats throughout the world. Modeled after the older tuna clipper,

Fig. 82. *Gypsy Queen.* This salmon boat hauls its seine by a power block on the main boom and stows it, not on a reel, but on a turntable. Boats like these make fishing Alaska's leading industry. *Gypsy Queen* fishes from Hoonah on Icy Strait in Alaska's Inside Passage.

Fig. 83. Tuna Purse Seiner. *Oficina Mapoche* fishes for tuna off the Chilean coast. The crow's nest, typical of pelagic fishermen, gives the lookout a wide horizon as he watches for sign of tuna. Sea birds feeding on schools of bait fish may indicate larger fish beneath, driving the bait to the surface.

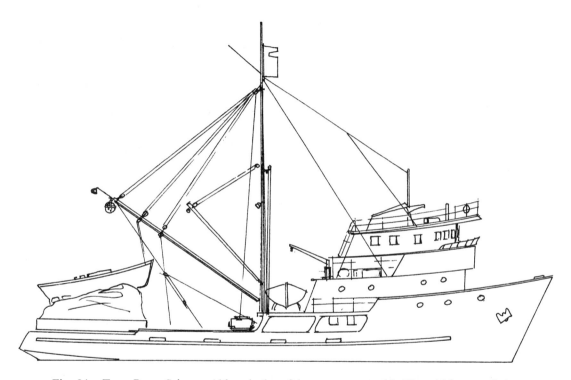

Fig. 84. Tuna Purse Seiner. Although they fish oceans apart, this West African craft is strikingly similar in silhouette to the Chilean seiner in figure 83. The high bow, tall mast and boom amidships, and clear sternsheets fit the purse seiner for its job.

which it has to some extent replaced in the U.S. fleet, it shows many clipper characteristics. High bow and forward deckhouse make a good sea boat for distant water operations. The wide stern supports a net platform and workboat rather than the clipper's bait tank and fishing galleries. The boom still handles the workboat but mounts a power block

Fig. 85. Norwegian Seiner. The European seiner resembles the side trawler rather than the Pacific seiner. The engine and deckhouse are aft in this Norwegian boat. The seine is handled amidships by a power block or deck edge net hauler.

as well for retrieving the seine. Below are brine tanks for cold storage of the catch.

Figure 83 shows the 83 foot seiner *Oficina Mapoche*. Cosmopolitans, she and three sister ships were designed in the United States, built in West Germany, and fish in Chile. Although their range is 6000 miles at ten knots, they are designed for shorter voyages in the waters off northern Chile. Refrigeration equipment can handle 120 tons of tuna in brine tanks. Intended primarily for the tuna fishery, they can also take anchovy by seine or can be modified for trawling.

Designed in Britain to operate in West Africa, *Amanzule* (fig. 84) shows many similarities to the Chilean boats. Larger and slightly faster, she measures 127 feet overall and grosses 333 tons. An 8 cylinder diesel provides 860 horsepower for a service speed of 11 knots. The extensive hydraulic equipment is powered by a 30 horsepower electric hydraulic pumping unit. The two-ton power block mounted on the boom end hauls the seine. There is a winch for the purse line and another for the topping lift, while two additional vang winches position the boom athwartships. The catch is stowed in ten brine wells. The fish can be held in brine just below freezing, frozen hard at 18° Fahrenheit, or stored dry after deep-freezing.

Some U.S. tuna boats are even larger. *Day Island*, a converted mine layer, claims a capacity of 1000 tons of tuna together with one of the world's largest seines, 580 fathoms long and 52 deep. Japanese tuna seiners often work from mother ships. Since the mother ship stores the catch and supports the catcher boats, the latter can be relatively small. Some are carried on board the mother ship; others steam to the grounds on their own power. Japanese tuna boats are not confined to the Pacific. They are found in the Indian Ocean and to a growing extent in the Atlantic. Russian tuna seiners are active in the Gulf of Aden, sending the catch home by mother ships and fish carriers.

HERRING BOATS

Pioneered by the Norwegians, the purse seiner is coming to dominate the herring fisheries off Iceland and in the

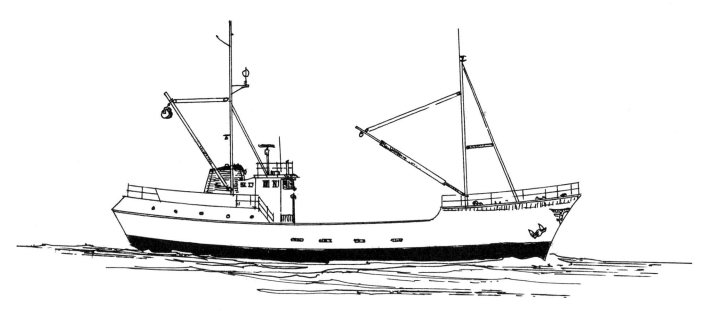

Fig. 86. Icelandic Seiner. This new craft includes the most modern features: bow and stern thrusters, telescopic boom for power block, ice-strengthened hull, refrigerated hold, and suction fish pump. Built in Norway, *Høfrunger III* operates from Husavik on Iceland's north coast. She fishes in the Greenland Sea for herring, either for food or for processing into meal and oil.

North Sea. Together with the midwater trawl, the seine is replacing the less efficient drift net. The first purse seiners were converted from other types simply by adding a power seine block and a skiff. They were generally successful, but their large catches and heavy blocks and seines made them

Fig. 87. Peruvian Seiner. This small seiner is bringing aboard its catch of anchovies by hand brail. She is built to typical Pacific design with house forward, seine deck aft.

top-heavy. At least seven craft capsized before the necessary design improvements were adopted. Second-generation craft are safer, more stable, and more efficient. Greater beam and depth, bluffer bows, deck-mounted net haulers, and stronger construction increase stability. Thrusters help control the ship during hauling operations and eliminate the

skiff and its crew. Hydraulic winches and blocks do the work of still other crew members.

Figure 85 shows a modern 125 foot Norwegian seiner. Engine and deckhouse are aft as in a trawler, rather than forward as in the California tuna boat. Her fish hold amidships carries 300 tons of herring. The pursing winch and net hauler are forward. A fish-finder helps locate the midwater herring shoals.

Figure 86 shows a new 130 foot Icelandic seiner, similar in design to the Norwegian boat. Her hull is strengthened for ice navigation. A power block mounted on a telescopic boom handles the seine. Transverse thrusters are located forward and aft. These are hydraulically driven propellers on athwartships shafts. In combination with the main propeller and rudder, the thrusters can hold the ship on any desired heading even against the pull of the seine. This craft has a refrigerated hold for herring destined for the table. Other holds, unchilled, stow herring for processing into meal and oil. The catch is taken on board and stowed by brailing or by suction pumps.

Britain is entering the purse seine field by converting several trawlers in Norwegian yards. The modifications include a hydraulic plant to drive power block, fish pump, and cargo winch; a net stowage; and a diesel workboat.

OTHER SEINERS

The purse seine is used in fisheries throughout the world where pelagic species occur in large schools in the upper reaches of the ocean. *Anchoveta* seiners give Peru the

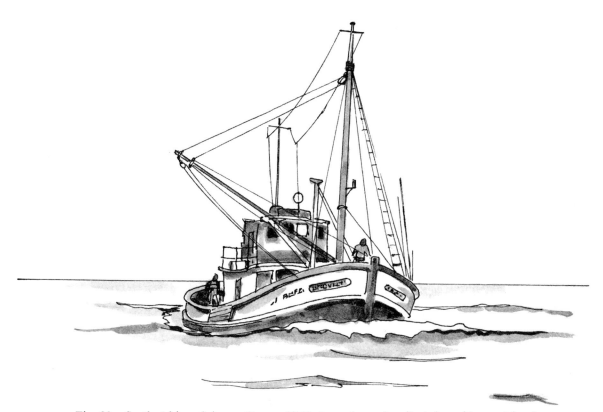

Fig. 88. South African Seiner. *Groenveld II* steams home heavily laden with a catch of pilchard. Diesel powered, this 90-tonner fishes up to 150 miles offshore. Her lines resemble those of Norwegian rather than Pacific craft.

world's largest annual catch and Chile one of the largest. These seiners are of the United States western type: deckhouse forward, high mast and boom with power block, net and skiff stowage aft. Many were built in the United States or more recently in South America to U.S. designs. Craft range in size from 50 to 100 feet, with capacities to 150 tons. Figure 87 shows a Peruvian seiner brailing anchovies with the aid of a seine skiff. The catch is processed ashore into fish meal for export to the United States and oil for Holland, Germany, and other European countries.

South African seiners (fig. 88) take large catches of pilchard, menhaden, anchovy, and mackerel for reduction into meal and oil. The total catch exceeds the U.S. menhaden catch, America's largest. The African grounds lie chiefly off the west coast, with Capetown and Walvis Bay as the main ports. Seiners are relatively small, with after deckhouse, low freeboard, and high stayed mast. The fleet contains modern craft such as the fiber glass *Western Dawn*. Built in 1963, she measures 67 feet overall and makes 11 knots on 220 horsepower. Fitted with fish-finding and echo-sounding sonar, she has a hydraulically operated power block to handle the seine.

In the United States, mackerel seiners operate from ports in California and New England. A typical Boston seiner resembles a dragger without gallows and with a crow's nest and heavy towing boom. She carries two boats, a large seine skiff to hold the net and a dory to assist. On sighting mackerel the seiner launches the boats and tows them from the boom end. At the edge of the school the dory is cast off with one end of the seine. Still secured to the boom, the seine boat pays out the net as the seiner encircles the fish and returns to the dory. The seine boat takes corkline and purse line on board, purses the seine with a power winch, and hauls in the wings. Now the seiner moves alongside the bunt to load the catch. The mackerel are iced down, layer by layer, one ton of ice to every two or three tons of fish. The usual cruise lasts about three days: one day out, one day on the grounds, and one day back to market.

VI. Harpooners

Whaling—the most important harpoon fishery—has risen and fallen at the mercy of wars and technology. Primarily an American trade, whaling grew during Colonial days, and in 1775 a large seagoing fleet fished the North and South Atlantic. In the War of the Revolution the Royal Navy swept Yankee whalers from the seas. With the restoration of peace the fleet regained its size and entered the Pacific. The War of 1812 again decimated American whaling, but it recovered rapidly until in 1842 over six hundred whalers flew the Stars and Stripes. These comprised more than three fourths of the world's whaling fleet. The development of oil wells and the outbreak of the American Civil War brought an end to whaling in the old style. Mineral oil, cheaper and more plentiful, destroyed the market for whale oil; Confederate raiders destroyed most of the whaling fleet. In five months of 1864 the C.S.S. *Shenandoah* alone took 38 ships on the northern Pacific grounds.

Whaling revived with the invention of steam propulsion and the harpoon gun. Half a dozen countries outfitted flotillas that operated in far southern and northern waters. The ships were so effective that they reduced whale stocks to the danger point. International conservation measures have been adopted to prevent extermination of the commercial species, but the industry has become increasingly less profitable and several countries have abandoned it.

Fig. 89. Harpoon. The detachable lily iron, five inches long, is secured to an 18 foot shaft.

SWORDFISHERMEN

New England fishermen have traditionally taken swordfish by harpoon. In the past they worked from sailing craft, rugged gaff-rigged sloops with crow's nest for the lookout

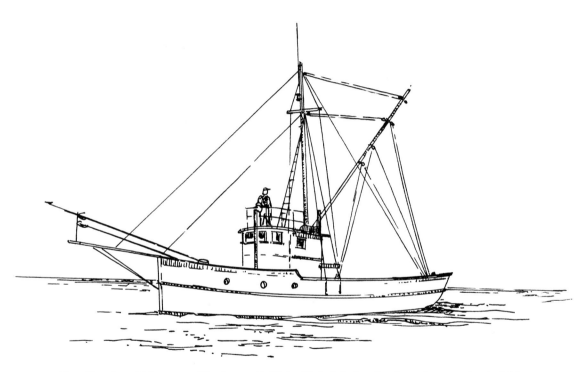

Fig. 90. Swordfisherman. Wooden craft 35 to 80 feet in length, these harpoon boats take swordfish from New Jersey northwards. When swordfish are not running, the boats may shift to trawling, gill netting, or running lobster pots.

Fig. 91. Sloop-rigged Swordfisherman. The forerunner of the motor craft in figure 90, this sailboat has the same harpooner's pulpit as well as a high perch for the lookout. Like the Seychelles shark boat (fig. 59) she carries a gaff-rigged mainsail and two headsails.

and pulpit for the harpooner (fig. 91). Today diesel boats have taken over. They retain the pulpit and high mast for good visibility aloft. A small steadying sail reduces rolling in a seaway. The helmsman's rudder and throttle are duplicated atop the deckhouse or at the masthead. On sighting a dorsal fin breaking water, the lookout takes control and

Fig. 92. Pulling Whaleboat. Like the boats carried by sailing whalers a hundred years ago, oar-driven whaleboats still take whales and mantas in the Azores and Seychelles. The whaleboat hull is double ended and single banked, that is, manned by one rower with one oar on each thwart. The helmsman's steering oar gives greater maneuverability than a rudder.

steers for the fish. The harpooner, balancing his 15 foot lance, mans the bowsprit pulpit. Alongside his quarry, the harpooner spears the swordfish quickly before it can sound. Once embedded, the harpoon head or "lily" pulls free of the shaft (fig. 89). Secured to the lily is a long heavy line which the crew make fast to a cleat on deck or to a keg. The keg is thrown overboard and followed by the boat. It may take several hours before a 500 pound swordfish can be played out and hoisted aboard.

Figure 90 shows a modern power boat from Martha's Vineyard. Engine and deckhouse are forward, fish hold aft. The winch and boom are fitted to handle the heavy catch, usually by a line around the tail. Vineyard men have been harpooners since the days of the whalers. Many are Wampanoag Indians whose forebears took to the sea in colonial times.

Swordfish are also caught by longliners who have begun operations off both United States seaboards. Pelagic longlines take heavy catches of tuna, marlin, and sailfish as well —all popular big game fish. Sport fishermen see a threat to their pastime and to the livelihood of the offshore charter boat fleet. This group includes hundreds of boats and crews, and their interests demand attention together with those of the commercial fishermen. A solution remains to be found.

WHALERS

For over a hundred years sailing whalers carried out their dirty, dangerous trade, bringing whale oil from distant oceans to light the lamps of Europe and America. Until petroleum products, and later electricity, destroyed the market for whale oil, and steam and iron replaced canvas and wood, the whalers fished the world over from the tropics to the ice fields. A typical whaler was a brig or bark, with good sailing lines but also with large holds to stow the casks of oil (fig. 93). Furnaces were mounted on deck for "trying" blubber to produce whale oil. The more valuable sperm oil was scooped out of the head cavities of sperm whales or cachalots. On deck were the whaleboats, double-

Fig. 93. Bark-rigged Whaler. The bark was square-rigged on fore and mainmast, fore and aft on the mizzen. She carried six whaleboats to harpoon the whales, and sailed alongside the carcass to load the blubber. At Mystic Seaport in Connecticut is preserved the last of the whalers, the *Charles W. Morgan*. A working whaler for eighty years, she made thirty-seven cruises and sailed in every ocean.

ended pulling boats for tracking and harpooning the whale (fig. 92). Fast and seaworthy, these boats could survive a "Nantucket sleigh ride" at the end of a harpoon line towed by a 90 foot sperm. Such ships are gone, but working whaleboats survive in the Azores and the Seychelles where shore-based whalers still pursue and harpoon whales and mantas in the traditional way.

Fig. 94. Harpoon Gun. Mounted in the bows of a whale catcher, the harpoon gun is far more effective than the hand-thrown lily iron. The projectile explodes after penetrating the whale, killing the whale and expanding the barbs.

British and American whalers, already operating in the Atlantic, moved into the Pacific in the late eighteenth century. After the British ship *Amelia* rounded Cape Horn in

1788 and the New Bedford craft *Rebecca* followed in 1791, whalers flocked to the west coast of South America, to Australian waters, and to the offshore grounds in mid-Pacific. Charts of the South Pacific still show *vigias*—hazards to navigation whose positions or even existence are doubtful— reported a century ago by the whalers. These are carried on the charts until a survey locates them or disproves their existence. The U.S. Navy Sailing Directions for the South Pacific apologetically explain that whaling captains did not care where they were so long as there were whales in sight.

Modern whale factory ships (*see* Chapter VII) still produce whale oil and sperm oil, but they also utilize the rest of the carcass, formerly discarded. Bones are ground into meal, skin is tanned for leather, liver is processed for vitamins, and meat is frozen for animal and human consumption. Modern fleets have become so efficient that whale stocks are in danger of extinction. Through international agreements some species have been protected, minimum sizes set, and catch limits established.

As a part of the conservation effort, the U.S. Bureau of Commercial Fishery carries out a whale marking program. Cruising off the coast of Southern California during the annual winter migration, observers count the whales en route from the Bering Sea to their wintering grounds along the coast of Baja California. Certain of the whales are marked with an eight inch stainless steel tube. Fired from a specially constructed shotgun, the harmless whale mark carries instructions to return the marker to the National Institute of Oceanography in Great Britain. As marks are recovered from

Fig. 95. Japanese Whale Killer. *Toshi Maru 17* works from a mother ship in Japan's Antarctic Whaling Expedition. The catwalk allows the harpoon gunner to reach his post on the
forecastle when high seas sweep the main deck.

whaling ships and stations, scientists are able to study the population, migration, longevity, and mobility of various whale species.

WHALE KILLERS

Whale killers or whale catchers operate either from factory ships or from shore stations. The greatest number are found in the Antarctic Whaling Expeditions—the name given to the annual movement of whale fleets to far southern waters. In the 1963-64 season (the Antarctic summer), sixteen factory ships operated a total of 192 catcher boats. Of the fleets, seven were Japanese with 78 catchers; four Russian with about 70 catchers; four Norwegian with 33 catchers; and one Dutch with 11 catchers. Great Britain, formerly a whaling nation, sold her two fleets to Japan, and Holland has recently followed suit. Russia and Japan also operate mother ships and fleets of killer boats in the North Pacific.

Fast and seaworthy, whale killers range from 60 feet for shore-based craft to 200 feet in the Antarctic expeditions. Figure 95 shows *Toshi Maru No. 17*, a modern Japanese diesel catcher boat grossing 760 tons. She is built for finding and killing whales in the world's roughest waters. A high crow's nest gives the lookout a wide horizon. The bridge too is high, for good visibility and for seakeeping in rough weather. Radio keeps the skipper in touch with the whale factory and with spotter aircraft. A catwalk leads to the forecastle and the harpoon gun (fig. 94). From it the harpooner shoots a 6 foot shaft with an explosive head. Detonated by a time fuse after it hits, the charge kills the whale and expands the harpoon points. The 6 inch harpoon line is then taken to a winch to haul the whale alongside. The catcher boat pumps the carcass full of air to keep it afloat and marks it with a radar reflector. After radioing to the factory ship the time of catch, species, and identification mark, the catcher casts it adrift and goes after another. A tug collects and catches and tows them to the factory ship. The time received, length, sex, and other details are logged. International Whaling Commission regulations require that the carcass be hauled on board the factory ship within 33 hours after it has been harpooned. This rule, intended to prevent waste from deterioration of the carcass, and other conservation measures are enforced by International Whaling Inspectors who travel with each fleet.

VII. Support Ships

As fishing fleets extend their operations to distant waters they must make a basic decision: should each boat head for home as soon as its fish hold is full, or should it transfer the catch to another vessel for transport to market and resume fishing? The world's fishing nations answer this question in different ways. The decision affects design of the craft as well as the composition of the fleet and the mode of operation.

At one extreme is the single ship which steams from home port to fishing grounds, fishes until its capacity is reached or its endurance expires, then returns either to home port or to a market nearer the grounds. Such a ship needs good seakeeping qualities, long endurance, adequate crew, and a means of preserving the catch. An early example was the New England whaler. Sails eliminated the requirement for fuel and, handled by iron crews, gave those wooden ships almost unlimited endurance. Sound design, skillful construction, and good materials enabled them to face the roughest seas. Whale oil would keep for long periods. As a consequence whalers could economically sail from New Bedford or Marblehead around Cape Horn into the North Pacific for a cruise lasting months or even years before returning to New England with all casks full.

A modern counterpart is the tuna boat from Southern California. Pole-and-line clippers and to an increasing extent purse seiners, they operate as far south as the equator. Economical diesels and large fuel tanks give them long range, while large (by U.S. fishing boat standards) size and

Fig. 96. Russian Factory Stern Trawler. The Russian fleet on the Grand Banks includes large craft like this trawler, fishing for whiting, cod, and haddock.

ample stores give long endurance. The clippers catch their own bait, and refrigeration preserves the catch. Large holds allow the boats to make valuable catches justifying long expensive voyages.

The opposite concept is that of the distant-water fishing fleet. Such a fleet includes not only the catcher boats but also mother ships, factory ships, refrigerated transports,

Fig. 97. Transferring the Catch. Here a catcher boat transfers a load of king crab to its mother ship.

oilers, and sometimes repair ships, water carriers, floating drydocks, tugs, and fishery protection vessels. The fleet may operate in waters half a world away from home. Japan, for example, has kept a small fleet in the northwest Atlantic, and Norway has operated whaling fleets in the Antarctic.

The fishing craft stay on station, transferring their catch to factory ships (fig. 97). Supplies are brought out to the catcher boats and the catch returned to base by support ships.

Russia and Japan have the world's largest operations; smaller fleets have been organized by Portugal, Spain, Norway, Holland, and Great Britain. Figure 98 shows the locations of these fleets in recent years.

The Bering Sea king crab fishery is typical of an operation in waters not too remote from home. In 1964 two Japanese fleets fished in Bristol Bay, a distance of about 2500 nautical miles from base at Hakodate. The requirement for this fishery was for a ship able to receive and process the catch and to furnish supplies, fuel, and minor repairs to enough catcher boats to meet the season's production goal. The requirement was met by the *Tokei Maru* and *Dainichi Maru* fleets. *Tokei Maru* is a combination mother ship/factory ship grossing 5400 tons. She carried eight 30 foot motor skiffs or *kawasakis*. Accompanying her were six larger catcher boats of about 80 tons, capable of steaming from home port to the grounds. *Dainichi Maru* is slightly larger, 5850 tons gross, and carried nine skiffs. Her fleet included six 80 ton catcher boats. Remaining together during transits and operations, each fleet was self-supporting and needed no other auxiliary ships. Sailing from Japan in early March, the fleets together canned over 5 million pounds of crab meat by mid-September.

Figure 100 shows a typical Japanese crab factory ship. Built on freighter lines, she has large holds for storing the catch and booms for taking aboard and unloading it. Fitted

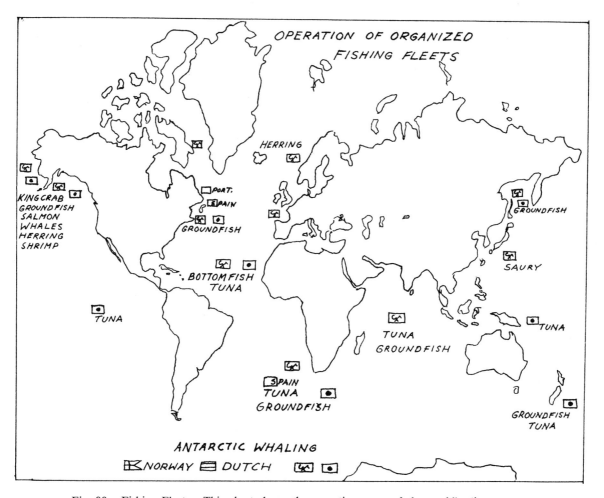

Fig. 98. Fishing Fleets. This chart shows the operating areas of the world's distant-water fishing fleets.

with cooking, canning and freezing equipment, she carries a large crew to man the processing plant. Racks for drying tangle nets are characteristic of this type. A Russian crab cannery ship of the *Zakharov* class (fig. 99) is much larger (12,700 gross tons and 530 feet overall) and supports 12 skiffs plus her fleet of catchers. Besides a crew of 150, she

Fig. 99. *Zakharov* Class Crab Factory. Russian craft like this factory ship compete with Japanese in the North Pacific king crab fishery.

carries 500 cannery personnel who work on a three-shift basis. Her production is triple that of the Japanese craft. She cans, manufactures fish meal and oil, processes caviar, and makes ice. These ships have been reported to remain on station for as long as a year.

Additional Japanese fleets work distant grounds in the Pacific and the Atlantic. Besides the crab fleets, the Bering Sea supports about a dozen others. Some catch shrimp; some take bottom fish with trawl, bottom set nets, or longlines; some are whalers. Some of the factory ships concentrate on production of fish meal and oil, while others process fish for human consumption. Japan operates tuna mother ships ranging in size up to 8800 gross tons with fleets of 55 catcher vessels. Expanding from the Pacific, her Atlantic tuna fleets take a large share of the total Atlantic catch. In 1964 eleven salmon mother ships operated in the North Pacific with 369 catcher vessels. Other fleets fish for saury in the North Pacific, sea bream in New Zealand waters, and whales in the Antarctic.

The Soviet fishing fleets have expanded manyfold since 1945, particularly in the last ten years. In the Far East, for example, over 200 new fishing vessels grossing half a million tons joined the fleet. The average tonnage per new ship in 1963 was 4253 tons. By comparison, the average new American fishing vessel in 1964 was a 50 ton craft, the largest 800 tons. The new Russian vessels include such huge ships as the whalers *Vladivostok* (17,150 tons) and *Sovietskaia Rossia* (33,150 tons). Figure 101 shows one of the two *Vladivostok* class. Built in West Germany, they are just under 600 feet long. Supported by a fleet of killer boats, they can process 1700 tons of raw whale per day into oil, meal, vitamins, and frozen meat. Twenty new refrigerator vessels have brought the fleet total to 70 "reefers." These

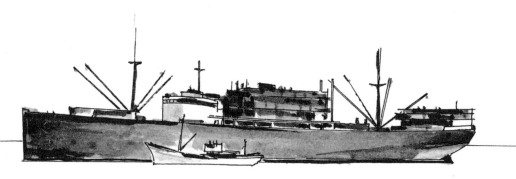

Fig. 100. Japanese Crab Factory. The 80 ton catcher boat alongside emphasizes the large size of this factory ship. She also carries eight *kawasakis* (fig. 74). Besides supporting her catcher boats, the mother ship is equipped to freeze, cook, and can their catch. In 1965 Japan sent fourteen factory ship fleets to the Bering Sea.

Fig. 101. Russian Whaler. This *Vladivostok* class mother ship handles the catch of nine killer boats. Whales are hauled up the stern slipway for processing into oil, meal, and frozen meat.

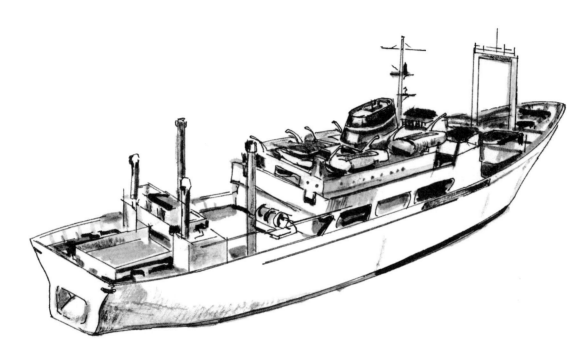

Fig. 102. Refrigerated Fish Transport *Skryplev*. The slipway in this Russian ship is designed for retrieving buoyed trawls. Trawlers, after completing their hauls, tie off and buoy the cod ends, leaving them adrift for recovery by the support ship. A radar reflector on the buoy allows *Skryplev* to locate the catch after dark or in reduced visibility. She can either freeze or process the catch.

Fig. 103. Refrigerated Shrimp Transport. *Atlantic Comet,* a new vessel, was especially designed for the Caribbean. She carries frozen shrimp from small shrimping ports in the Guianas, Venezuela, and Windward and Leeward Islands to processing plants in the United States.

Fig. 104. *Gil Eannes.* The mother ship of the Portuguese Grand Banks cod fleet, *Gil Eannes* provides services for 5000 fishermen and their craft. Her facilities include hospital, recreation room, and chapel. She also repairs machinery and transports frozen fish.

range in size from the 270 foot overall, 2500 gross ton *Bratsk* class, of East German manufacture, to the larger *Sevastopols*, Russian built vessels 430 feet long grossing 5500 tons. The newest type is the Danish constructed *Skryplev* class (fig. 102). Three-hundred-footers grossing 4700 tons, they can freeze fish or process the catch into meal and oil, storing the products until a full load is transported back to a Russian port. The *Skryplevs* are fitted with stern ramps for hauling aboard buoyed trawl nets.

Fig. 105. Icelandic Fishery Protection Vessel. *Odinn* renders assistance to Icelandic fishing boats and protects Iceland's valuable grounds from foreign boats. Iceland restricts the waters inside a 12 mile limit to her own fishermen. Icelandic grounds outside the 12 mile limit supply almost one third of Great Britain's demersal catch, and smaller portions of Germany's and Norway's. Fishing rights are often a matter of dispute, and claims vary from nation to nation.

They need not rendezvous with the trawler; the latter merely ties off and buoys the cod end of its trawl, marking the buoy with a radar reflector. This technique permits transfer of the catch even in weather too rough for the trawler to come alongside.

In waters off Alaska the Soviet fleets in September 1965 numbered seven. In the Gulf of Alaska were two groundfish fleets: one including 41 trawlers, 10 refrigerator transports, 1 factory ship, and 1 tanker; the other 27 trawlers, 5 transports, 1 tug, and 1 cargo vessel. In the Aleutians were two more fleets: 12 trawlers and 3 reefers in the central region and 14 trawlers, 2 reefers plus other support vessels to the west. Off the western Aleutians were three whale fleets comprising 3 factory ships and about 27 whale killers. Operating 150 vessels in the far North 2000 miles from home port demonstrates that the U.S.S.R. is indeed a first-class maritime nation.

The Portuguese Grand Banks cod fleet is supported by the mother ship *Gil Eannes* (fig. 104). Owned by the Codfish Ship Owner's Guild and registered in Lisbon, she is named for a Fifteenth Century Portuguese navigator. Each spring she sails west to tend the 100 ship, 5000 man fleet. Besides refrigerated holds for fish transport, she is equipped with a 75 bed hospital, chapel, library, and recreation room. A machine shop, storerooms, and towing gear cater for mechanical trouble in the fleet, and a Portuguese naval officer is embarked to deal with international fishery problems. *Gil Eannes* was built in 1955. Of 5000 gross tons burden, she is fitted with two 1500 horsepower diesels giving a speed of 13 knots.

The U.S. registered refrigerator transport *Atlantic Comet* (fig. 103) specializes in the expanding shrimp trade. Equipped for carrying refrigerated, chill, and general cargo, she is one of a fleet of nine vessels especially designed for

Fig. 106. Japanese Fishery Inspection Boat. This 45-foot launch can make 15 knots, enough speed to overhaul most fishing craft in the near grounds. With a six man crew, she works for the Prefecture of Kanagawa in central Honshu.

carrying frozen seafood from small Caribbean ports to U.S. processing plants.

A different type of support craft is the fishery protection vessel. Fishing rights have long led to international friction, and a tendency to extend the limits of territorial waters has aggravated the issue. Several nations have found it necessary to employ fishery protection vessels to prevent foreign craft from fishing in national waters. They play a secondary role in protecting national fishing craft both from perils of the deep and from fishery protection vessels of other countries. Iceland, dependent on her fisheries and surrounded by fleets of many nations, assigns fishery protection as a primary mission of its Coast Guard. Figure 105 shows *Odinn*, one of its newest vessels. Danish built, she displaces 1000 tons, steams at 18 knots, and mounts a 57 mm. gun. Peru, whose *anchoveta* fishery makes her one of the world's leading fishing nations, has six British-built Vosper patrol boats. Twenty-five knot 110-footers, these craft are fitted with the most modern gear including two machine guns, extensive electronic equipment, and anti-roll fins. Figure 106 shows a Japanese fishing inspection boat. A 20 ton 45 foot launch, her twin 145 horsepower diesels drive her at 15 knots.

VIII. Research Vessels

The term research vessel is something of a misnomer. These craft carry out not only, or even primarily, basic research, but usually a combination of research and the related functions of exploratory fishing, fishing gear development, and equipment evaluation. Typical basic research projects are determination of fish swimming speed, discovery of migratory information through fish and whale tagging, and ecological investigations. Exploratory fishing is the search for new grounds where fish can be taken in commercially rewarding quantities. Gear development embraces the improvement and evolution of fishing equipment. Evaluation involves the comparative testing of different equipment in statistically designed experiments to determine how well each catches fish. Because of the variety of tasks performed as well as the tendency to utilize whatever ship becomes available, research vessels vary widely in design. Some are simply commercial fishing boats chartered for the duration of a research project. Others are conversions of fishermen, yachts, and surplus naval ships. The best are new craft designed and built from the keel up as fishery research vessels.

An example of chartered craft is the trawler *Paragon*. Working for the U.S. Fish and Wildlife Service in 1964,

she conducted exploratory shellfish trawling and dredging in the Aleutian Islands. She also tested underwater television for visually observing sea life. Figure 108 shows the French trawler *Thierry*. With a similar craft she was chartered for

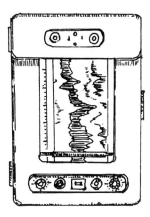

Fig. 107. Fish-finder. This electronic echo sounder shows the depth of water as well as the presence of schools of fish directly beneath the ship.

the UNESCO Guinean Trawling Survey by the United States and United Kingdom. Special equipment was added to

Fig. 108. Trawler *Thierry*. This French craft is modified for research work. She is fitted with refrigerator, extra electric power supply, and hydrographic winch.

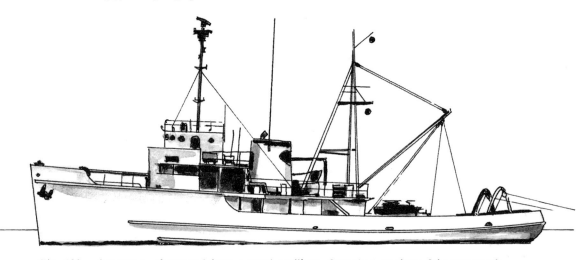

Fig. 109. *Geronimo*. Converted from a naval auxiliary, *Geronimo* conducts fishery-research for the U.S. Bureau of Commercial Fisheries. Here she tows a stern trawl. She also carries gear for trolling and hook-and-line fishing.

prepare the 114 foot diesel craft for research in tropical waters. Each received refrigerated storage, an auxiliary engine, a.c. alternators, air conditioning, and a hydrographic winch. These craft sought exploitable fisheries in the Gulf of Guinea on the west African Coast and prepared reference collections of the fish of that area.

War surplus ships have been converted for fishery research by a number of American universities and by the Bureau of Commercial Fisheries. *Geronimo* (fig. 109) began life as a naval auxiliary. A 147 foot research vessel, she is now outfitted for trawling, trolling, and pole-and-line tuna fishing. In addition she has the scientific equipment necessary for oceanographic, hydrographic, and weather observations.

The Commercial Fishing Bureau craft *Anton Bruun* was converted from the presidential yacht U.S.S. *Williamsburg*; *Undaunted*, from a Navy tug. *Trident*, a research vessel belonging to the University of Rhode Island, was originally an Army maintenance and supply vessel. Scripps Institute of Oceanography of the University of Southern California operates two former pleasure craft, the schooner *Velero IV* and *Gerda*, a Danish yacht built on trawler lines.

The post-1945 interest in all phases of oceanography has provided funds in many countries for new construction. Designed as research vessels, some are especially equipped for fishery research; others for physical, chemical, biological, or geological oceanography. Figure 111 shows the exploratory research vessel *John N. Cobb*. Launched in 1950, she was expressly designed for exploratory fishing in the waters off Alaska and the United States Pacific Northwest by the Bureau of Commercial Fisheries. *Cobb* is modeled after a Pacific Coast purse seiner, measuring 93 feet × 25 feet × 9 feet with a 10 knot cruising speed. Main propulsion is furnished by a 500 horsepower diesel, while two 45 horsepower auxiliary units drive generators, main trawl winch,

Fig. 110. *Pathfinder*. This small research craft operates in Chesapeake Bay. She belongs to the School of Marine Science and Research of the College of William and Mary.

and hydraulic pump. Speeds up to 3 knots are available through a clutch which disconnects the propeller from the main engine and connects it through a chain drive and reduction gearing to one of the auxiliary engines. Equipment is available for a variety of fishing methods. Gallows on each quarter allow stern trawling. Hydraulically powered gurdies are used for hauling longline gear, and a live tank holds bait for tuna pole-and-line fishing. Outriggers can be stepped for

107

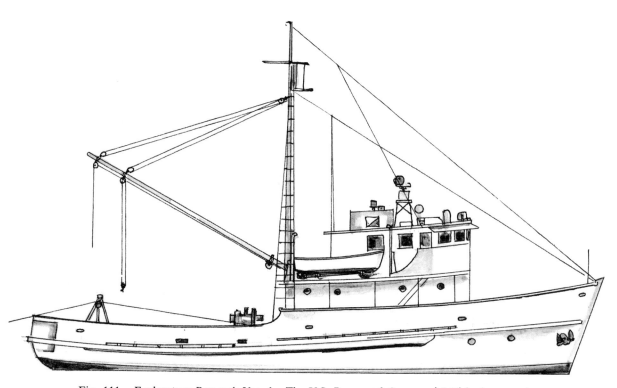

Fig. 111. Exploratory Research Vessel. The U.S. Bureau of Commercial Fisheries operates *John N. Cobb* in the Pacific Northwest. She is named for the founder of the School of Fisheries at the University of Washington. Launched in 1950, she is one of the veterans of the research fleet.

trolling, and a 17 foot workboat extends the range of operations into shallow water. The main winch and cargo boom can handle trawling or seining gear. Oceanographic instrumentation includes plankton nets, bathythermographs, bottom sampling devices, and reversing-type thermometers. Refrigeration facilities allow *Cobb* to carry about 50,000 pounds of frozen fish, a small quantity for commercial purposes but ample for research work. Her electronic installation provides two fathometers, radar, loran, radio direction finder, and two radiotelephones. This flexible installation has allowed *Cobb* to conduct exploratory fishing for albacore, scallop dredging, trawling for groundfish, shrimping, and pelagic trawling.

Figure 110 shows a smaller but newer vessel, the 55 foot diesel *Pathfinder*. Intended for work in Chesapeake Bay, she is operated by the School of Marine Science of the College of William and Mary. Other new American craft are *Wolverine*, a 46-footer working for the University of Delaware; *Atalantis II* of the Woods Hole Oceanographic Institution; and the Bureau of Commercial Fisheries' *Albatross III*, *David Starr Jordan*, and *Townsend Cromwell*. The latter, built in 1964, includes such novel devices as an underwater viewing chamber for observation of fish at close range.

Other countries have launched oceanographic craft which work to a greater or lesser extent on fishery research. Figure 113 shows (a) *Thalassa,* a French research vessel built on the lines of a stern trawler; (b) *Discovery II* of Great Britain's National Oceanographic Council; (c) *Shoyu Maru*, a Japanese tuna longliner type; and (d) *Konstantin Boldyrev*, a Russian exploratory trawler.

Small submarines, developed by most of the world's fishing nations, permit scientists and research workers to

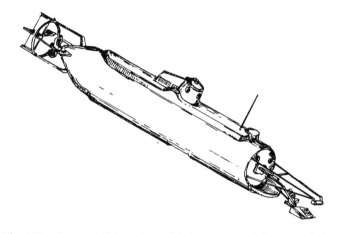

Fig. 112. Research Submarine. This Japanese craft has operated as deep as 1000 feet. Diesel-electric propelled, she runs her diesel engine on the surface and switches to an electric motor for diving. Four underwater lights permit visual observations in the perpetual darkness of deep waters. The lights also attract fish which scientists can trap in a controllable cage on the bow.

extend their observations to the depths of the sea. French Commandant Cousteau's *Soucoupe* was one of the first. More recently built, *Alvin*, *Aserah*, and *Cubmarine* work on

American oceanographic projects. The Russian *Atalant* and the British *Mobell* have been used for observation of trawls. The Japanese midget submarine *Yomiuri* (fig. 112) is one of the largest. Built to take a crew of six men to 1000 feet, she is 47 feet overall and can make four knots. She is fitted with observation ports, floodlights, and television as well as a hydraulically operated "hand" and a cage for trapping specimens. Small submersibles are improving steadily in performance and flexibility, and a nuclear propelled fishery research submarine seems to be on the horizon. These craft are destined for a role of ever increasing importance in studying and improving the world's fisheries.

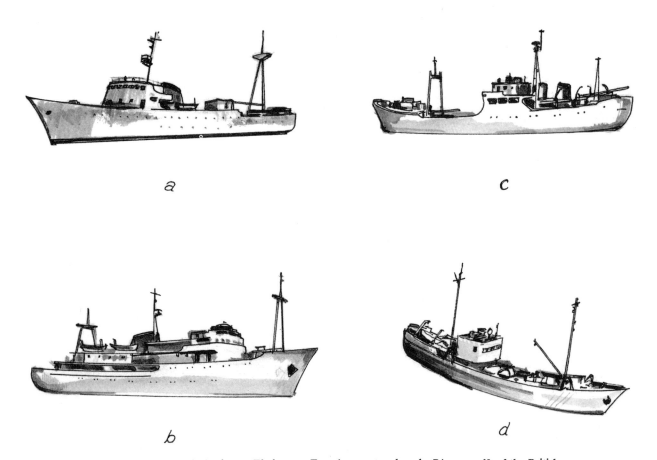

Fig. 113.   Research Craft.   a. *Thalassa,* a French stern trawler;   b. *Discovery II,* of the British National Oceanographic Council;   c. *Shoyu Maru,* a Japanese longliner;   d. *Konstantin Boldyrev,* a Russian side trawler.

IX. Small Boats

Small boats play a large role in the world's fisheries. In the underdeveloped countries they are the only fishing craft. Even in countries with large distant-water fleets the lone fisherman and his boat produce an important part of the catch. In the United States in 1960, for example, there were 130,000 fishermen utilizing 77,000 boats, an average of less than two men per boat. Of the 503 boats added to the fleet in 1964, over 40 per cent were less than 40 feet long.

One of the most common uses of small boats is tending fish traps. In the bluefin tuna fishery, traps line the Mediterranean coasts of Spain, France, Sicily, and Tunisia. Some spots have had traps for decades or even centuries. Each May and June schools of tuna pass along these coasts to their spawning grounds, returning in the opposite direction during the summer. To take these fish, long walls of webbing, reaching from the surface to the sea bottom, are buoyed and anchored in place. Extending from the beach to the 10 to 35 fathom curve, the nets sometimes reach six miles in length. A series of funnel shaped openings lead the fish into a bag enclosed on the bottom as well as the sides.

During migrations, fleets of a dozen small boats and thirty to fifty men work the traps daily. Two six-man rowboats herd the tuna through the successive compartments into the bag of the trap, closing the entrance by a flap. Two larger boats fitted with winches and booms then begin to haul aboard the ends of the bag with the aid of other pulling boats that have encircled it (fig. 116). As the bag grows smaller, the fishermen harpoon or club the tuna and

Fig. 114. Portuguese Dory. A flat-bottomed seaworthy boat, the dory has fished the Banks of the northwest Atlantic for centuries. Their construction permits dories to be nested in stacks on deck. Europeans usually fish one man to a boat; American dories were manned by a crew of two.

pull them on board. A good catch yields seven or eight hundred tuna of over 150 pounds.

Another important trap fishery is based on the pound nets of Chesapeake Bay. Introduced into the United States around 1850, the pound net spread from New England southward to Maryland and Virginia. Over a thousand nets ring the

Bay and produce a large percentage of its edible catch. Each net is tended by a "deadrise" towing a large skiff. Together they haul the bag and empty the catch each morning at slack water. Figure 115 shows a typical deadrise. Vee-bottomed with a transom stern, it has its engine aft and a small deckhouse forward. The same type boat serves for oyster tonging, running crab pots, and trotlining.

Figure 117 shows another American craft, the pirogue of the Louisiana marshes. The "Cajun" fisherman sets his fish traps and trotlines from these shallow draft double-enders which, he boasts, will float in a heavy dew.

Long a seafaring nation, Portugal is heavily dependent on fishing. Chapter III discussed the Grand Banks dory (fig. 114). Besides the distant-water fleet, inshore craft work from the Atlantic beaches. Figure 118a shows a *barco do mar* landing through the surf. Large flat-bottomed pulling boats, their design is traditional. Tides on the Portuguese coast have a wide range, and boats must be pulled well above the water's edge. Oxen supplement manpower in dragging the largest *barcos* up the beach.

Figure 118b shows the type of one- or two-man boats that fish from the harbors of the French Riviera. These double-ended bateaux have a straight stem and outboard rudder. Brightly painted, even the smallest has its name in bold letters on the bow. Although fitted with small engines, they are often rowed, the oars working on thole pins rather than rowlocks.

Canoes occur in one form or another in Africa, Asia, Oceania, and America. Dugout canoes are built in whole

Fig. 115. Tonging Oysters in the Chesapeake. The waterman scoops oysters from the mud in up to three or four fathoms of water. He dumps his catch on a culling board, picks out the oysters, and washes the mud and trash over the side. His boat is a deadrise.

114

Fig. 116. Mediterranean Tuna Trap. These boatmen are concentrating the tuna in the bag of the net in preparation for capture. The large boats haul in the net; the smaller boats herd and boat the fish.

or in part from a single tree trunk. In some boats only the bottom and bilges are made from the trunk, the sides being planked over ribs. In others the single tree forms the entire boat. Fitted with sails, canoes are tender because of their narrow beam and lack of a keel. Caribbean and some Far Eastern canoes rely only on internal ballast and skillful seamanship to avoid capsizing. Others gain stability by adding outriggers or a twin hull. Polynesian, Micronesian, and

Fig. 117. Pirogue. This fisherman is setting a hoop net in a Louisiana bayou.

Ceylonese canoes usually have a single outrigger (fig. 118c). They can be paddled or sailed. Surprisingly seaworthy, outriggers have crossed thousands of miles between Pacific islands. Tanganyikan fishermen, on the east coast of Africa, use port and starboard outriggers for added stability (fig. 118d). The *jangada* of the Brazilian fisherman is a twin-hulled catamaran.

The Accra canoe (fig. 118e) is used in the coastal fisheries in West Africa's Gulf of Guinea. A 26 foot sailing dugout, it can hold nine men, one hundred fathoms of gill net, and a ton of fish. The method of fishing is unusual: the net is shot in a circle around a school of surfaced herring. The crew then jump overboard into the ring of the net. Splashing and paddling, they drive the herring into the net where they are caught by the gills. The crew climb aboard, haul the net, and return ashore. The catch is removed from the net after the boat is beached.

Fishing sampans fill the harbors of the Orient (fig. 120). Smaller than junks, they step a single mast with a battened sail. A raised deckhouse amidships shelters the crew. Long sculls propel the sampan when the wind dies and in close quarters. Motors are gradually being fitted to increase speed, range, and hence catch.

The British Isles and the Pacific Northwest both lie on the eastern shores of large oceans. Both are influenced by warm currents, the Gulf Stream in the Atlantic and the Japanese Current in the Pacific. The climates of the two regions are similar, and so are many of their fishing craft. Figure 119a shows a Scottish lobster boat; figure 119b a Dungeness crabber from Puget Sound. The lobster boat is 28 feet long with house and engine aft in typical British style. Her working deck is forward, with space for a good supply of lobster pots and a capstan for raising them. A short mast, well aft, carries the steadying sail.

The crab boat has most of the same features, but they are arranged differently. The house is forward and the working space aft, just opposite from the lobsterman. A davit and winch amidships raise the pots, which are stowed aft. Somewhat larger, the crabber may travel several hundred miles to the grounds and has a live well to keep the catch fresh on the trip to the cannery.

Fig. 118. Inshore Fishermen. a. Portuguese *barco do mar* landing in Atlantic surf; b. Boats of the French Riviera; c. Ceylonese single outrigger; d. Double outrigger from Tanganyika; e. Accra canoe fishes gill nets on West African coast.

a

b

Fig. 119. Crab and Lobster Boats. a. Scottish lobster boat with engine and house aft; b. Puget Sound crabber, a larger boat for longer trips.

118

Fig. 120. Chinese Sampan. The sampan has a single mast with a four-sided sail. Chinese preserve fish by drying them in the sun (foreground).

Fig. 121. Mussel Dredge. Mussels are an important fishery in the Netherlands. Some are cultivated on mussel farms; others dredged by boats like this.

Glossary

Aft—towards the stern of a ship

Amidships—midway between bow and stern of a ship, or on the centerline

Asdic—British and European term for sonar, from Anti-Submarine Detection Investigating Committee

Athwartships—perpendicular to the centerline; the opposite of fore and aft

Auxiliary—a boat fitted with both sails and engine

Beam—the width of a ship

Block—a pulley, consisting of one or more "sheaves" rotating on a shaft between the frame or "cheeks"

Boom—a horizontal spar to which the foot of a fore and aft sail is bent, or a spar fitted with tackle to handle cargo (fig. 123a, e, f)

Bowsprit—a fore and aft spar extending forward of the bow of a sailing vessel

Bunt—the portion of a seine in which the fish are confined after the wings are hauled

Cable—a measure of length equal to 200 yards

Capstan—a rotating cylinder, with vertical axis, for hauling in a rope or line (fig. 122)

Carvel built—planked with strakes that butt against each other to form a smooth side

Fig. 122. Capstan.

Clipper bow—a bow whose profile extends sharply forward from the waterline, as in a clipper ship

Clinker built—planked with overlapping strakes; lapstrake

Cod end—the long narrow cylinder at the trailing end of a trawl, tied at the after end with the cod end knot

Controllable pitch propeller—a propeller in which the pitch of the blades can be adjusted to drive the ship ahead or astern at the desired speed. The propeller r.p.m. are constant

Counter—the vertical or near vertical planking forming the stern of a boat

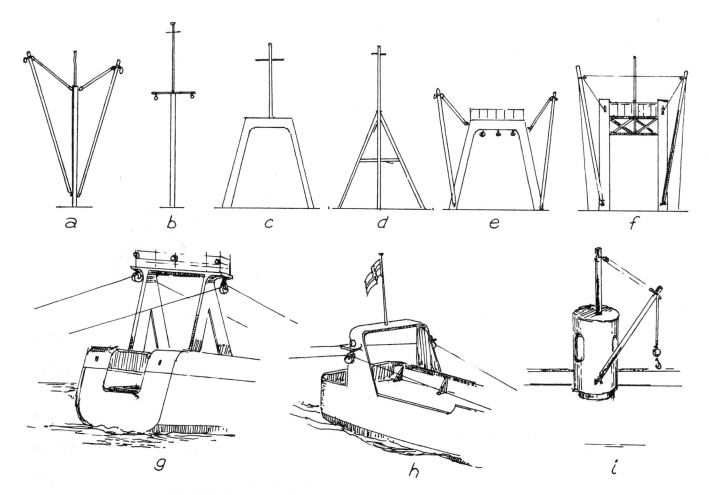

Fig. 123. Uprights. a-d. Masts; e-f. Kingposts; g-h. Gantries; i. Crane.

Cran—a Scottish measure of volume equal to 45 gallons

Deadweight tonnage—a measure of weight of a ship's cargo equal to the difference between light displacement and loaded displacement (DWT) (fig. 127)

Diesel electric propulsion—the system for propelling a ship in which diesel engine(s) drive a generator which in turn drives a motor coupled to the screw

Displacement—a measure of the weight of a ship, equal to the weight of the water displaced in tons

Draft—the vertical distance from keel to waterline

Echo sounder—an electronic device for locating fish and measuring depth of water by acoustic ranging

Endurance—the number of days that a ship can remain at sea or the number of miles that it can steam during that period

Fantail—the after deck of a ship

Fathom—a measure of length or depth equal to 6 feet

Fathometer—an electronic device for measuring the depth under a ship or boat

Fishery—a collective term including the fish, fishing grounds, equipment, and business for taking fish commercially

Fish-finder—an electronic device for locating schools of fish by acoustic echo ranging

Fleet—a string of nets secured end-to-end

Forward—towards the bow of a ship

Fyke net—a long bag-shaped net

Gaff—a spar to which the head of a quadrilateral fore and aft sail is bent

Gallows—an inverted U-shaped frame from which a trawl block is suspended

Gantry—an athwartships frame, often movable or pivoted, from which blocks or gear are suspended (fig. 123g, h)

Gross tonnage—a measure of the volume of all enclosed spaces on a ship expressed in gross tons of 100 cubic feet (fig. 127)

Gurdy—a power operated device for hauling in a fishing line, used on longliners or trollers

Gypsy head—a small capstan attached to a windlass

Kingpost—a short mast usually associated with a cargo boom (fig. 123e, f)

Kit—a British measure equal to twelve stones or 168 pounds

Knot—a measure of speed equal to one nautical mile or 1.15 statute miles per hour

Length between perpendiculars—length of a ship measured at the load waterline

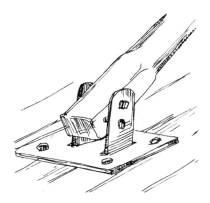

Fig. 124. Mast in Tabernacle. A tabernacle permits lowering a mast to increase stability and allow passing below bridges.

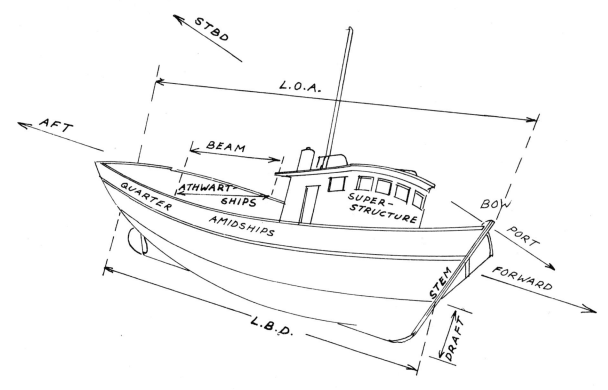

Fig. 125.   Nomenclature of a Fishing Boat.

124

Live well—a tank of sea water in which fish are kept alive while en route from the grounds to port

Mesh size—the distance between opposite corners of a square of mesh when stretched diagonally, expressed in inches or millimeters

M.F.V.—British abbreviation for motor fishing vessel

Net tonnage—a measure of the volume of all earning spaces (i.e. holds, cargo tanks, etc.) on a ship expressed in net tons of 100 cubic feet (fig. 127)

Point—an angular measure equal to 11¼ degrees; thus 32 points make a full circle, 8 points 90 degrees

Port—the left side of a ship looking forward

Prawn—shrimp

Processing plant—a factory whose input is raw fish and whose output is fish meal, oil, and other fish products

Quarter—the sides of a ship aft of amidships and forward of the stern

Radar—an electronic device for locating and tracking objects by reflection of electromagnetic energy; from radio detection and ranging

R. D. F.—radio direction finder; an electronic device for determining the bearing of a radio signal

Running lights—navigational lights burned by ships and boats while underway. See figure 129 for lights of fishing vessels

Russian ship designations—Abbreviations for the Russian names of different types of fishing vessels are used as part of the bow number and in the literature. The most important are: BRT Large refrigerator trawler (Б PT);

BMRT Fish factory trawler (Б MPT); SRT Medium trawler (CPT); SRTR Medium refrigerated trawler (CPTP); SRTM Medium freezer trawler (CPTM).

Screw—a ship's propeller

Service speed—the maximum speed that a vessel can maintain for long cruises

Fig. 126. Block and Tackle.

Sheer—the rise in a ship's deck at bow and sometimes stern

Shoot—referring to nets, to set or lay

Sonar—an electronic device for locating and tracking underwater objects by reflection of acoustic energy; a type of fish-finder

Stability—the resistance of a ship to overturning

Starboard—the right side of a ship looking forward

Stay—a wire or fiber rope used to support a mast

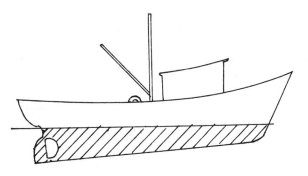

LIGHT DISPLACEMENT = 15 LONG TONS

DEADWEIGHT TONNAGE = (LADEN) MINUS (LIGHT) = 20T.
(LONG TONS = 2240 lbs.)

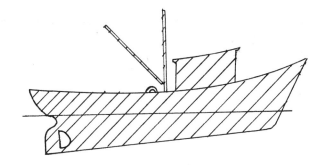

30 TONS GROSS

GROSS TONNAGE = VOLUME OF ALL ENCLOSED
SPACES. "TON" = 100 CUBIC FEET

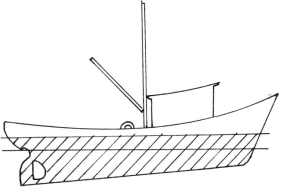

LADEN DISPLACEMENT = 35 TONS

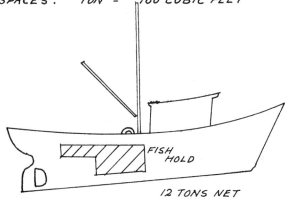

FISH HOLD

12 TONS NET

NET TONNAGE = VOLUME OF ALL EARNING
SPACE.

Fig. 127. Tonnages.

Stem—the vertical timber or structure at the bow to which the sides are attached

Stone—a British measure of weight equal to 14 pounds

Superstructure—the upper works of a vessel

Tabernacle—a pivoted mast step allowing the mast to be raised and lowered (fig. 124)

Tackle—the rope led through a set of blocks to form a purchase (fig. 126)

Try net—a small trawl used to locate good catching grounds before setting the main trawl(s)

V. H. F.—abbreviation for very high frequency voice radio

Warp—a long line, specifically one used for towing a trawl, or an anchor line

Whitefish—a British term for North Sea groundfish

Winch—a rotating cylinder with horizontal axis for hauling in a line or rope (fig. 128)

Windlass—a device for hauling in an anchor chain

Fig. 128. Winch. This low pressure hydraulic winch handles the warps on a large trawler.

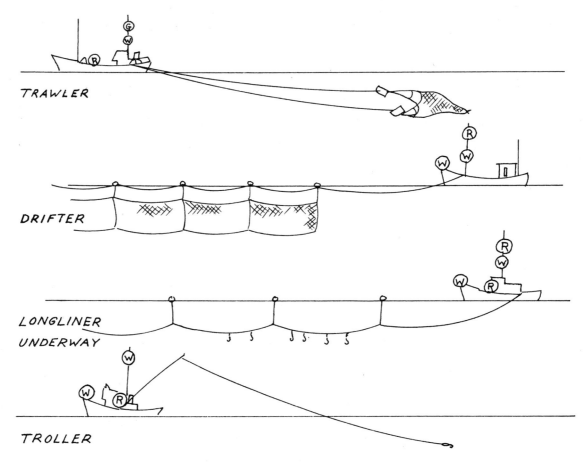

TRAWLER

DRIFTER

LONGLINER
UNDERWAY

TROLLER

Fig. 129.   Running Lights for Fishing Craft.

128

Bibliography

Each of the books, reports, and periodicals in this list contains information on commercial fisheries, fishing boats, or gear. In a few, fishing boats or gear is the main topic, but most are wider in scope, dealing with additional aspects of a particular fishery or commercial fishing in general. Where the title is not self-explanatory, a note tells what information the reference includes.

BOOKS

Alverson, D. L., et al, "A Study of Demersal Fishes and Fisheries of the Northeastern Pacific Ocean" (Vancouver: Institute of Fisheries, The University of British Columbia, 1964).

Blackman, Raymond V. B., *Jane's Fighting Ships* (edited in Great Missenden, Bucks, England; supplied in the U. S. A. by McGraw Hill Book Co., New York; published biennially). Fishery protection vessels.

Bloomster, Edgar L., *Sailing and Small Craft Down the Ages* (Annapolis, Maryland: U. S. Naval Institute, 1940).

Borgstrom, G., and Heighway, A. J., *Atlantic Ocean Fisheries* (London: Fishing News (Books) Ltd., 1961). Catching, processing and marketing.

Braynard, Frank O., *The Story of Ships* (New York: Grosset and Dunlap, 1960).

Burgess, J., *Fishing Boats and Equipment* (London: Fishing

Fig. 130. Gulf Shrimp Boat. This Campeche trawler has hoisted one main trawl bag to the starboard masthead. A try net swings from the port masthead prior to rigging over the stern. The main trawls are towed from the port and starboard outriggers.

News (Books) Ltd., 1962). A guide for the practical operating commercial fisherman.

_____ *Mechanization of Small Fishing Craft* (London: Fishing News (Books) Ltd., 1963).

Chase, Mary Ellen, *Fishing Fleets of New England* (Boston: Houghton Mifflin and Co., 1961).

Church, Albert Cook, *American Fishermen* (New York: W. W. Norton and Co., Inc., 1940). Text and photographs of New England sailing craft.

Dodman, Frank E., *Observer's Book of Ships* (London: Frederick Warne and Co., Ltd., 1958). An outstanding pocket guide worth every shilling of its small price.

Fishing Boats (London, H. M. Stationery Office, 1960). Photographs and descriptions of British sailing craft models.

Fishing News Directory and Equipment Guide (London: Fishing News (Books) Ltd., Annual). Primarily British in scope, but there is information on equipment of interest to all.

Garner, J., *Deep Sea Trawling and Wing Trawling* (Glasgow: Gourock Rope Works, Ltd., 1960).

_____ *How To Make and Set Nets* (London: Fishing News (Books) Ltd., 1962).

Grant, Leonard J., *Wondrous World of Fishes* (Washington: National Geographic Society, 1965).

Hardy, A. C., *Seafood Ships* (London: Crosby Lockwood & Son Ltd., 1947).

Hardy, Sir Alister, *The Open Sea: Its Natural History* (Boston: Houghton Mifflin Co., 1959).

Hodgson, W. C., *The Herring and Its Fishery* (London: Routledge & Kegan Paul).

Hodson, A., *Introduction to Trawling* (London: Fishing News (Books) Ltd., 1964).

Kristjonsson, H., *Modern Fishing Gear of the World* 1 (1962) 2 (1964) (London: Fishing News (Books) Ltd.). These two volumes are the results of FAO Congresses on fishing gear and are technical in nature.

Landström, Björn, *The Ship* (Garden City, New York: Doubleday and Co., Inc., 1961).

Morgan, Robert, *World Sea Fisheries* (London: Methuen and Co., Ltd., 1956). An excellent general coverage.

New Fishing Boats in Japan (Tokyo: The Fishing Boat Association of Japan, 1965).

O'Farrell, R. C., *Lobsters, Crabs and Crawfish* (London: Fishing News (Books) Ltd., 1960). Catching and marketing.

Oliver, R. C., *Trawlerman's Handbook* (London: Fishing News (Books) Ltd., 1962).

Stansby, Maurice E., *Industrial Fishery Technology* (New York: Reinhold Publishing Company, 1963).

Travis, William, *Shark for Sale* (New York: Rand McNally and Co., 1961).

Tressler, Donald K., and Lemon, James McW., *Marine Products of Commerce* (New York: Reinhold Publishing Co., 1951).

Truang, Jan-Olaf, *Fishing Boats of the World* I (1955) II (1961) III (1967) (London: Fishing News (Books) Ltd.) These volumes contain technical papers and discussions resulting from Fishing Boat Congresses, organized by the FAO, in 1953, 1959 and 1965.

Tucker, D. G., *Underwater Observations Using Sonar* (London: Fishing News (Books) Ltd., 1964). Basic knowledge for the fishing vessel skipper and the layman.

Villiers, Capt. Alan, et al, *Men, Ships, and the Sea* (Washington, D. C.: National Geographic Society).

von Brandt, A., *Fish Catching Methods of the World* (London: Fishing News (Books) Ltd., 1964).

Ward, G., editor, *Stern Trawling* (London: Fishing News (Books) Ltd., 1964).

Wick, Carl I., *Ocean Harvest (The Story of Commercial Fishing in Pacific Coast Waters)* (Seattle: Superior Publishing Co., 1946).

Wilson, G., *Scottish Fishing Craft* (London: Fishing News (Books) Ltd., 1965).

ARTICLES, REPORTS AND PAPERS

Alverson, D. L., "Fishing Vessels Around the World," *U.S. Naval Institute Proceedings,* January, 1961.

Cobb, David, "The Sailing Thonniers," *Yachting World,* December, 1962.

Commercial Fishing Gear of the United States (Washington: Fish and Wildlife Service, Circular 109, 1961).

Commercial Fishing Vessels and Gear (Washington: Fish and Wildlife Service, Circular 48, 1957).

Craig, R. E., "The Fisheries Application of Sonar"; paper at Sonar System Symposium, Birmingham University, England, 1962.

Duncan, David D., "Capturing Giant Turtles in the Caribbean," *National Geographic Magazine,* August, 1943, pp. 177-190.

Fiedler, Reginald H., et al, *The Fisheries and Fishery Resources of the Caribbean Area* (Washington: Bureau of Commercial Fisheries, Fishery Leaflet 259, 1957).

Fisheries of the United States—1964 (A Preliminary Review) (Washington: Bureau of Commercial Fisheries, Report No. C.F.S. 3800, April, 1965).

June, Fred C., *The Menhaden Fishery of the United States* (Washington: Fish and Wildlife Service, Fishery Leaflet 521, 1961).

Kassell, Comdr. Bernard M., U.S.N., "The Fishing Fleet of the Soviet Union," *U.S. Naval Institute Proceedings,* Nov., 1961.

Knake, Boris O., *Atlantic Coast Mackerel Purse Seine* (Washington: Bureau of Commercial Fisheries, Fishery Leaflet 373, 1950).

Lee, Charles F., *The Menhaden Fishery, Past and Present* (Washington: Fish and Wildlife Service, Fishery Leaflet 412, 1953).

Refrigeration of Fish, Parts 2 and 4 (Washington: Bureau of Commercial Fisheries, Fishery Leaflets 428 and 430 respectively, 1956).

Smith, Robert O., *Fishery Resources of Micronesia* (Washington, Fish and Wildlife Service, Fishery Leaflet 239, 1947).

Umali, Agustin F., and Wartel, Herbert E., *Reef Fishing* (Washington: Bureau of Commercial Fisheries, Fishery Leaflet 354, 1949).

United States Fisheries, 1964 (Washington: Bureau of Commercial Fisheries, Report No. C.F.S. 4098, April, 1965).

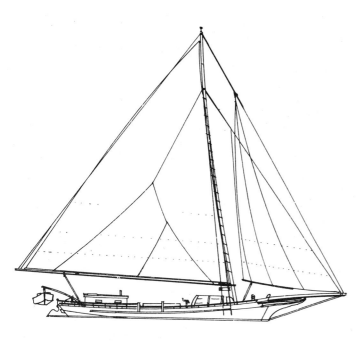

Fig. 131. Chesapeake Skipjack. Skipjacks have been saved as a boat type by the conservation laws of Maryland which permit dredging oysters only under sail. In recent years the industry has not prospered and the number of boats is decreasing.

COMMERCIAL FISHING PERIODICALS

Canadian Fisherman (Gardenville, P.Q.: National Business Publications). A monthly journal devoted to Great Lakes, East and West Coast Canadian Fisheries.

Commercial Fisheries Review (Washington: Bureau of Commercial Fisheries). A monthly devoted to U.S. international and foreign fisheries. Well illustrated.

Fish Boat/Seafood Merchandising (New Orleans: H. L. Pease Publications). Issued 13 times a year.

Fisheries Newsletter (Canberra: Fisheries Branch, Dept. of Primary Industry). Monthly.

Fishing Gazette (New York: Fishing Gazette Publishing Corp.) A monthly journal devoted mainly to United States fisheries.

Fishing News (London: Arthur J. Heighway Publications Ltd.) A monthly journal devoted primarily to British fisheries. Well illustrated.

Fishing News International (London: Arthur J. Heighway Publications Ltd.) A quarterly journal devoted to fisheries of the world.

National Fisherman (Combining: *Atlantic Fisherman, Maine Coast Fisherman* and *Pacific Fisherman*) (Camden, Me.) A monthly journal covering commercial fishing, boats and boatbuilding. U. S., and Canadian.

Norwegian Fisherman (Bergen: Toroff Holme.) A quarterly journal, in English, devoted to northern European and international fisheries.

Sea Frontiers (Miami: Institute of Marine Science). A monthly journal of oceanography, including a useful book review section.

Shipbuilding Equipment (London, Hulton Publications Ltd.). A monthly journal which often includes information on fishing vessels and their machinery.

World Fisheries Abstracts (Rome: FAO of the United Nations). A quarterly with editions in English, French and Spanish.

World Fishing (London: Grampian Press, Ltd.). A monthly journal, very well done, devoted primarily to British and northern European fisheries but with worldwide coverage as well.

Index

Index